Energy Flow in Biology

Energy Flow in Biology

BIOLOGICAL ORGANIZATION AS A PROBLEM IN THERMAL PHYSICS

Harold J. Morowitz

*Department of Molecular Biophysics
and Biochemistry
Yale University
New Haven, Connecticut*

OX BOW PRESS
Woodbridge, Connecticut
1979

First published, 1968

1979 Reprint published by
OX BOW PRESS
P.O. BOX 4045
Woodbridge, Connecticut 06525

ISBN 0-918024-12-9 (Hardcover)
ISBN 0-918024-13-7 (Paperback)
Library of Congress Card Number 79-89841

Printed in the United States of America

This book is dedicated to Lucille,
whose own efforts to seek order
in our immediate biosphere
have made possible this monograph
and much more

Preface

Much of this book was written in Hawaii where the warm, brilliant tropical sunlight provides a constant reminder of the overwhelming importance of solar energy flux in the operation of the living world. However, other parts of this book originated in New England, where, on cold winter nights, the roaring wood blaze in the fireplace serves in its own way as a reminder of our debt to solar energy flow.

This is a book about biology which, on first inspection, is curiously nonbiological. I have little to say about flora and fauna and even more surprising, I have little to say about helices, genes, mitochondria, and the rest of the fascinating hardware of life. It is not lack of interest in the mainstream of modern biology that has governed the selection of material, rather it is a desire to penetrate the wonderous diversity as far as possible and concentrate attention on those underlying principles which make possible the panorama of living forms. When the unifying ideas are sought, they are found to reside in the nature of atoms and the distribution of energy in the universe. On these dry bones are assembled the flesh and blood of life.

While this is in no sense a book on metabiology or an attempt at an ontological study of life, I have nonetheless entered this study with some preconceived philosophical ideas which in all fairness should be shared with the reader. I have assumed that biology is a manifestation of the laws of physics and chemistry operating in the appropriate system under the appropriate constraints. I have rejected the prebiological notion of "historical accident" as a kind of know-nothingness which renders further study impossible. Having made these philosophical judgements I will, with some difficulty, refrain from commenting on questions of meaning because the tools of science are still a bit coarse for such delicate matters.

This book is intended for research workers and graduate students in the biological and physical sciences who are seeking physical foundations for the principles of biology. To the biologist who finds the jargon and equations of statistical mechanics unfamiliar, I would suggest concentration on the nonsymbolic portions, for most ideas are stated both verbally and formally. The concepts are, in general, relatively simple and the use of mathematical procedures is largely an attempt to lay the groundwork for extending the ideas in a more quantitative sense.

The approach used in this book has been heavily influenced by contact with four men; two close personal friends, the third an acquaintance of but one meeting, and the last known only through his writings. The infectious enthusiasm of Ernest Pollard has given me the courage to speculate when it would have been more prudent to pursue more accepted modes of research. The quiet and gentle wisdom of Henry Quastler has been a continuing inspiration even after his untimely death. The writings and one personal encounter with Albert Szent-Gyorgi have provided an example par excellence of the power of buoyant optimism in approaching scientific problems. Erwin Schrödinger's book, "What is Life?", has been a constant intellectual stimulant prodding me to search the borderland between biology and physics.

Parts or all of this manuscript have been read by Frederick Forro, Jr., Edward Kerner, Robert Fuller, Carl Sagan, Ernest Pollard, and Edwin Taylor. I would like to extend my warmest thanks to these readers for their very substantial efforts. I would also like to acknowledge their stimulating and sometimes sobering comments. While I have not always heeded my readers advice, I have always taken it most seriously.

Many of the studies discussed in this book were supported by the Bioscience Programs of the National Aeronautics and Space Administration. That support is gratefully acknowledged.

This preface would be incomplete without a "mahalo nui loa" to the University of Hawaii Department of Microbiology for its hospitality during the period of the completion of this book.

HAROLD J. MOROWITZ

January 1968

Contents

Energy Flow in Biology

I
Biology and Thermal Physics

*The oneness of all life means that the same stream of life
energy runs through all the veins of the universe. It is
this stream which binds all life together making them one,
each being governed by its own particular laws which it must
obey. So while there are higher forms of life in other
worlds and human life is the highest form on this planet,
mineral life, plant life, animal life, human life and other
world life are one in their essence. A realization of this
Oneness should do much to eliminate discrimination, especially
against colour, race and caste.*

From "Essentials and Symbols of the Buddhist Faith"
by The Venerable E. K. Shinkaku Hunt

The purpose of this book is to discuss and present evidence for the general thesis that *the flow of energy through a system acts to organize that system*. The motivation for this approach is biological and has its origins in an attempt to find a physical rationale for the extremely high degree of molecular order encountered in living systems. From the study of energy flow in a number of simple model systems, we shall attempt to demonstrate that the evolution of molecular order follows from known principles of present-day physics and does not require the introduction of new laws. In addition, we shall note that the biological utility of existing theoretical physical chemical concepts becomes manifest when we turn from the restrictions of equilibrium thermodynamics and concentrate attention on the rich possibilities of nonequilibrium and steady state theory. Even equilibrium theory can acquire more biological meaning when we consider geological time scales and therefore allow an appreciably wider range of accessible states.

It is, thus, the plan of this work to examine certain aspects of biology in terms of the concepts of thermodynamics, statistical mechanics, and kinetic theory. Such an examination will, we believe, lead to a much closer relation between biology and physics and will make clearer the sense in which biological phenomena are ultimately consequences of the laws of physics.

By way of historical introduction, we may point out that it is now over one hundred years since the introduction of the theory of evolution in biology and the second law of thermodynamics in physics. Each of these principles has been a unifying and heuristic theory within its own science. Yet, the relationship of biology to physics has disclosed a slight antagonism between evolution and increasing entropy.

Biological evolution involves a hierarchical ascendency to more and more complex forms of living systems. The second law of thermodynamics asserts that the universe, or any isolated section of the universe that we choose to consider, is tending toward maximum entropy. Consideration of statistical mechanics as well as kinetic theory makes it clear that maximum entropy involves maximum disorder consistent with the constraints of the system. Thus, when we think of evolution within the context of the Boltzmann H theorem, we think of evolution to more and more disordered states of the system.

The physicist Bridgeman has commented on this tension between biology and thermodynamics (1): "The view that the universe is running down into a condition where its entropy and the amount of disorder are as great as possible has had a profound effect on the views of many biologists on the nature of biological phenomena. It springs to the eye that the tendency of living organisms is to organize their surroundings, that is, to produce 'order' where formerly there was disorder. Life then appears in some way to oppose the otherwise universal drive to disorder. What is the significance of this? Does it mean that living organisms do or may violate the second law of thermodynamics?"

The resolution of this apparent divergence between a biological and a physical theory is the realization that the second law of thermodynamics applies to systems that are approaching equilibrium, whereas the surface of the earth, the matrix of biological evolution, belongs to a different class of physical systems. Equilibrium systems require either isolation (adiabatic systems) or contact with a single fixed reservoir (isothermal systems). Most real physical systems are of another sort; they are in contact with more than one reservoir, some of which may be regarded as sources and some of which may be regarded as sinks. The description of these systems requires the consideration of the flow of either matter and/or energy from the sources through the systems of interest to the sinks.

Steady state systems constitute a special case in which the sources and sinks are fixed so that as the system ages, the flows from sources to sinks become constant, and the local intensive parameters of the systems (temperature, concentration, pressure, etc.) become time independent. In nonequilibrium systems, the exact significance of the intensive parameters is not always clear, especially in cases far from equilibrium. In any case, the macroscopically measurable parameters become time independent in the steady state.

The difference between equilibrium and steady state systems is that in the latter, there is a continuous net flow of either matter or energy through the system from and to external reservoirs. The steady state as well as other nonequilibrium systems are not characterized by entropy maxima and need not be considered within the narrow confines of the second law of thermodynamics. A body of theory has grown up in recent years attempting to characterize the precise formal requirements and conditions of the steady state. Works in this field (2, 3, 4) have been termed "steady state thermodynamics," "nonequilibrium thermodynamics," "irreversible thermodynamics," or simply "thermodynamics" by those who would apply the term "thermostatics" to traditional equilibrium theory.

Much of this monograph is an attempt to characterize certain non-equilibrium states and to show how they acquire properties that are very different from those that might be expected in the equilibrium state. These properties, in turn, have important implications for biology. The surface of the earth clearly belongs to that class of systems in contact with both an energy source and an energy sink. The source is, of course, the sun which is constantly irradiating the earth with a flux of photons. The sink is outer space. The night side of the earth radiates infrared energy. The significance of this process will be vividly recalled by those who have experienced nightfall on a high mountain or in the desert and have noticed the rapidity of the temperature drop. Gates (5) has expressed the flow of energy to and from the surface of the earth by an equation of the form:

Solar radiation flux + thermal radiation flux from the ground
+ latent heat of evaporation × rate of
evaporation
+ sensible heat flux by conduction from the
ground through the soil or rock to the
surface
+ sensible heat flux by convection in the air
+ a storage term for storing energy or giving
up energy over short periods of time = 0   (1-1)

If we take any appreciable period of time, the storage term has a zero average and the last term on the left-hand side drops out, indicating that the surface is in an approximate steady state. The storage term, of course, shows diurnal and seasonal variation due to the growth and consumption of photosynthetically synthesized products which act as energy storage reserves. The principal flow terms are solar radiation flux and thermal radiation from the ground. The solar radiation spectrum approximates that for a black body at 6000°K, while thermal radiation from the earth's surface also partially has the character of black body radiation at the particular local temperature. The Stephan–Boltzmann law indicates that the total energy radiated from a black body, J_{BB} is:

$$J_{BB} = \sigma T^4 \tag{1-2}$$

where σ is the Stephan–Boltzmann constant. At 20°C, $J_{BB} = 0.584$ cal cm^{-2} min^{-1}, which is a substantial heat loss. The detailed problem is of course complicated by cloud cover and many other difficult problems in atmospheric physics. However, the whole earth is in an approximate steady state with respect to radiation: the flux of solar radiation is balanced by the loss of energy to outer space.

To sum up our general introduction, we note that in order to study evolution or increasing organization as a physical process, we must depart from equilibrium considerations and examine the molecular physics of steady state and other nonequilibrium systems. This is not to assert that traditional equilibrium thermodynamics has no role in biology; the use of calorimetric and thermochemical concepts has already been of great utility in biochemistry and ecology. Indeed, in Chapters III–V we will make considerable use of the data of classical thermal physics. It is, however, the theme of this book that studies of nonequilibrium systems will lend considerable insight into the evolution and functioning of living systems. We shall find that the flow of energy is a self-organizing principle at both the macroscopic and the molecular level.

To provide a background for examining the energy flow principle, we shall first consider a particular model system which is designed to illustrate some of the limitations of equilibrium systems, and indicate the special areas of inquiry necessary to overcome these limitations and establish a biophysics, a theory of biology rooted in physics. Consider then a system which has the same atomic composition and volume as a given living cell and is in contact with an isothermal reservoir at some appropriate temperature. At equilibrium, what is the probability that this system will, in fact, be a living cell? While we must recognize at the outset that any attempts to answer this type of question in detail are at the moment impossible, nonetheless, useful insights can be gained from a study of the question and certain limiting statements that can be made. We can first give the question a less abstract formulation by use of a Gedanken experiment.

Suppose we were to grow a very large batch of cells of a bacterium such as *Escherichia coli*. We then centrifuge the cells into a tightly packed pellet of volume V containing N cells, transfer the pellet into a container of fixed volume V, and raise the temperature to some very high value (on the order of 10,000°C) so as to destroy any traces of the original chemical state of the system. Now slowly cool the system to 300°C and allow it to age indefinitely at this temperature. The system may now be considered as a group of subsystems of volume $v = V/N$; indeed, it constitutes a grand canonical ensemble* of such subsystems.

---

* Throughout this monograph, we will formulate our discussion in terms of statistical mechanics, thermodynamics, and kinetic theory. Hence, ensemble language is introduced without apology. While the primary purpose of this book is to discuss certain aspects of biology, we are committed to this examination in terms of the

If the ensemble were infinite, members would represent all possible physical states of the subsystems consistent with the constraints. It will be more convenient in subsequent considerations to use a canonical ensemble rather than a grand canonical ensemble. This can be achieved in our Gedanken experiment by subdividing the system into subsystems of volume v such that all subsystems have the same atomic composition. The subsystems are then separated by walls impermeable to matter but capable of conducting heat. Among the possible states of the system, some must correspond to living cells. This assertion is proven by the fact that the initial bacterial cells represent systems of the same volume, atomic composition, and temperature as the final members of the ensemble. As the initial cells were alive, this state is clearly a possible one for members of the canonical ensemble; although, as we shall see, such states have exceedingly small probabilities. Each possible state of the ensemble members may be designated the ith state having energy ϵ_i. The probability of the system being in the ith state at equilibrium is then:

$$p_i = \frac{\exp(-\epsilon_i/kT)}{\sum_j \exp(-\epsilon_j/kT)} \tag{1-3}$$

Since ϵ_i represents energy states rather than energy levels, we need not include a degeneracy term (6). The symbol k denotes the Boltzmann constant. We now introduce a biological Kronecker delta δ_{iL}. This function has the value 1 if the ith state is living and the value 0 if it is nonliving. The probability of a given member of the ensemble being in the living state is then:

$$p_L = \frac{\sum_i \delta_{iL} \exp(-\epsilon_i/kT)}{\sum_j \exp(-\epsilon_j/kT)} \tag{1-4}$$

At this point, we can place an upper bound on p_L by applying our knowledge of the chemical bonds found in actual living systems compared to the bonds found in the normal equilibrium state. It is then clear that δ_{iL} must equal zero for all $\epsilon_i < \epsilon_m$, where ϵ_m represents the minimum bond energy above the ground state energy for living systems. It can be noted that:

$$p_{L\,max} = \frac{\sum_{i=m}^{n} \exp(-\epsilon_i/kT)}{\sum_{j=1}^{n} \exp(-\epsilon_j/kT)} \tag{1-5}$$

physical sciences. The necessary background in physical science can be found in three widely available and excellent works by T. Hill (6), H. B. Callen (7), and J. C. Slater (8). Appendix I reviews some of the more important results of thermal physics that are used in this work.

If reasonable estimates of ϵ_m are possible, $p_{L\,max}$ may be calculated or at least a crude estimate may be obtained. Calculations based on Eq. (1-5) can, however, be only the roughest order of magnitude and must yield values of $p_{L\,max}$ that are much larger than p_L. The subject is nevertheless worth pursuing since even the extreme maximum turns out to be so vanishingly small that we are able to make limiting statements which are a useful introduction to energy flow problems in biology.

The ability to make a numerical estimate from Eq. (1-5) rests on the notion that ϵ_m can be determined or estimated. The existence of a minimum bond energy for living systems depends upon an empirical generalization from biochemistry (discussed in Chapter III) that all living systems have a large number of chemical features in common. To note a few, consider the amino acids of proteins, the nucleotides, intermediate phosphate compounds, and sugars. The distribution of covalent bonds in a living system is therefore a characteristic feature of that system, as is the heat of formation of those bonds. From a thermodynamic argument, it is possible to compute the difference between the heat of formation of a group of biochemical compounds and the heat of formation of the lowest energy state possible for a system of the same atomic composition, volume, and temperature; hence, on the basis of gross molecular composition, we can estimate the energy difference between biological systems and their corresponding equilibrium systems. This calculation will be carried out from different points of view in Chapters III and IV. Since the biochemistry of terrestrial life appears to be quite ubiquitous, the energy difference ϵ_m is, within fairly broad limits, a characteristic parameter of living systems as we know them.

In Chapter III, we shall set up a model system that will permit the calculation of $p_{L\,max}$. For the moment, we may anticipate the results of that calculation which shows that $p_{L\,max}$ is the order of magnitude of $10^{-10^{11}}$ for a typical bacterial cell. The reason for $p_{L\,max}$ having such an infinitesimally small value is that a living cell represents a configuration showing a very large amount of energy as configurational or electronic bond energy relative to the amount of thermal energy when compared with the equivalent equilibrium system. The living state has a very unlikely distribution of covalent bonds compared with the equivalent equilibrium state either at the same total energy or at the same temperature. The living state may be regarded as having a very high electronic temperature relative to its normal thermodynamic or kinetic temperature.[†] The concept of electronic temperature will shortly be made more precise. For the moment we note that living systems are at a high potential energy level. Here, we might anticipate one of our general conclusions. Living systems are at a high electronic energy because the absorption of solar photons produces high potential compounds. In the subsequent degradation of this energy to heat, a number of other high energy compounds are produced along the way, with the general result that the biosphere is at a relatively high level of potential energy when compared with the energetic ground state.

When one gets to probabilities of the order of $10^{-10^{11}}$, some problems might be anticipated from the fact that the usual formulation of statistical mechanics [Eq. (1-3)] assumes that the mean values and the most probable values of the number of systems in the ith state are the same (6). This poses some questions about states of the system very far removed from the most probable ones. The Darwin–Fowler method (10) calculates the mean distribution which, for very large ensembles, approaches the most probable distribution. When the probabilities become as vanishingly small as indicated earlier, large ensembles become too large to be conceptually meaningful (11). If we use Jaynes' formulation of statistical mechanics (12), which we will return to in Chapter VI, the very small probabilities pose no special problem and fit into the structure of the general theory. In any case, our purpose here is to note that the equilibrium probability is vanishingly small, and as we shall show in Chapters III and IV, this is so clearly the case that our discussion does not depend on the details of the theory.

Returning to the question of high electronic temperatures, we will discuss a simple model system that demonstrates this feature and anticipates the application of energy flow considerations to such systems. Consider a chemical reaction represented by a potential energy diagram of the type shown in Fig. 1-1. [In discussing chemical reactions, we will employ the formalism of absolute reaction rate theory (13).] Assume

---

† The kinetic temperature of any system is defined by the following formula:

$$\tfrac{3}{2}nkT = \sum_{i=1}^{n} \tfrac{1}{2}m_i C_i^2$$

where m_i is the mass of the ith atom and C_i is its velocity; k is the Boltzmann constant. This concept of temperature is derived from Chapman and Cowling (9). These authors note that "the kinetic-theory definition of temperature is applicable whether or not the gas is in a uniform or steady state, and therefore it provides a concept of temperature more general than that of thermodynamics and statistical mechanics, where only equilibrium states are considered."

that we have a reaction vessel with isomers B and C in an isothermal isobaric bath at temperature T. At equilibrium,

$$\frac{[B]}{[C]} = e^{-\Delta F/RT} \tag{1-6}$$

where ΔF is the Gibbs free energy change of the reaction and R is the

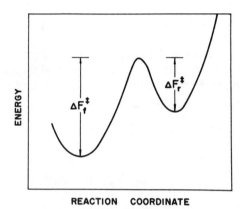

REACTION   COORDINATE

FIG. 1-1. Energy diagram for the transition between reactants and products according to absolute reaction rate theory. The reactants are in the left-hand potential well and require an activation free energy of $\Delta F_f^{\ddagger}$ to react. The products are in the right-hand potential well and require an activation energy of $\Delta F_r^{\ddagger}$ for the back reaction.

gas constant. The overall reaction represents a balance of a forward reaction proceeding at a rate

$$[C] \frac{kT}{h} \exp\left(-\frac{\Delta F_f^{\ddagger}}{RT}\right)$$

and a back reaction proceeding at a rate

$$[B] \frac{kT}{h} \exp\left(-\frac{\Delta F_r^{\ddagger}}{RT}\right)$$

where $\Delta F^{\ddagger}$ is the activation free energy and h is Planck's constant.

Next, irradiate the system with photons of appropriate energy to yield a photochemical transition from C to B. Assume that the flux is G photons per unit area per second and that the geometry of the vessel is such that they are all absorbed by C, yielding a conversion to B. Assume also that the back reaction proceeds by collisions of the second kind (inelastic collisions) and involves no radiation but a conversion to thermal energy. The system will eventually reach a steady state, heat will be transferred to the reservoir, and the following condition will obtain.

$$h\nu G = a(T' - T) \qquad (1\text{-}7)$$

ν is the frequency of the radiation, a is the thermal transfer coefficient per unit area from the vessel to the reservoir, and T' is the steady state temperature of the irradiated system.

Equation (1-7) expresses the condition of the steady state that the amount of energy flowing into the system is to equal the amount leaving the system. If V_A is the volume per unit surface area of the vessel, the forward and back reactions now proceed at the rates:

$$V_A[\text{C}']\frac{kT'}{h}\exp\left(-\frac{\Delta F_f^{\,*}}{RT'}\right) + G, \quad \text{forward}$$

and

$$V_A[\text{B}']\frac{kT'}{h}\exp\left(-\frac{\Delta F_r^{\,*}}{RT'}\right), \quad \text{back}$$

In the steady state these rates are equal, and

$$\frac{[\text{B}']}{[\text{C}']} = \frac{k_1 M + G/V_A}{k_2 M - G/V_A} \qquad (1\text{-}8)$$

where M is the total concentration of C and B in the system and k_1 and k_2 are rate constants of the form

$$\frac{kT'}{h}\exp\left(-\frac{\Delta F^{\,*}}{RT'}\right)$$

Substitute $G = gMV_A$, where g is the flow of photons per molecule.

$$\frac{[\text{B}']}{[\text{C}']} = \frac{k_1(T') + g}{k_2(T') - g} \qquad (1\text{-}9)$$

The equilibrium ratio of B to C at temperature T' in the absence of irradiation would have been

$$\frac{k_1(T')}{k_2(T')} = \exp\left(-\frac{\Delta F}{RT'}\right) \qquad (1\text{-}10)$$

The actual value is higher than this and corresponds to an effective electronic temperature T'' which can be obtained from:

$$\frac{[\text{B}']}{[\text{C}']} = \frac{(kT'/h)\exp(-\Delta F_f^{\,*}/RT') + g}{(kT'/h)\exp(-\Delta F_r^{\,*}/RT') - g} = \exp\left(-\frac{\Delta F}{RT''}\right) \qquad (1\text{-}11)$$

To obtain the same ratio of [B] to [C] in the absence of a photon flux it would have been necessary to take the system to a higher temperature T'', as can be seen from Eq. (1-11). The concentrations in the steady state system, therefore, correspond to the chemical state of an equilibrium system at a higher temperature. It is this feature that is characteristic of biological systems.

In more complex systems, it is not always possible to calculate a single T'' which will describe the energy distribution of the system. The concept is clear, however, if we consider the usual approximation that the energy of a system may be broken up into electronic, translational, rotational, and vibrational energies.

$$\epsilon = \epsilon_e + \epsilon_t + \epsilon_r + \epsilon_v \qquad (1\text{-}12)$$

In the chemical systems we are discussing, energy will be distributed among the possible energy levels in a Maxwell–Boltzmann distribution for translation, rotation, and vibration. This distribution will define a temperature of the system and will be the kinetic temperature or the measured temperature by most kinds of thermometers. Energy will be distributed in the electronic levels in such a way that the upper levels will be more populated than would be expected for a Maxwell–Boltzmann distribution at the system temperature. This is all that we shall generally imply by the concept of elevated electronic temperatures.

Note that in the previous model system, the condition of high electronic energy was maintained by a flow of energy through the system. Such a system without energy flow would eventually decay to a Maxwell–Boltzmann distribution of energy, although the process might take a very long time. This accords with our thesis about energy flow and will subsequently be developed as a more general case.

Next, let us return to the number $10^{-10^{11}}$ which requires some discussion as many people are not accustomed to dealing with such infinitesimally small numbers. The number may be written $10^{-100000000000}$ or as a decimal; it may be written as a decimal point followed by 99,999,999,999 zeros followed by a 1. The number occurred as the maximum probability of a given ensemble member being alive. Suppose we have an ensemble of W members and we sample it at the rate of X times per second for Y seconds. We may then ask the question: what will be the probability of a living member having occurred once? This will be $p_L WXY$. To place our argument in the context of terrestrial biology, let us assume the maximum possible values of W, X, and Y for the surface of the earth.

(a) $W_{max} = 10^{100}$. This is a very generous estimate of the number of atoms in the universe and must, therefore, represent an outside upper limit to the numbers of members of the ensemble.

(b) $X_{max} = 10^{16}$ sec^{-1}. Since we are dealing with atomic processes, sampling times cannot be appreciably shorter than times for atomic processes which have a lower limit of about 10^{-16} sec.

(c) $Y_{max} = 10^{18}$ sec. Assume that the age of the universe is ten billion years, which appears to be an upper limit from current estimates.

Utilizing these estimates, $W_{max}X_{max}Y_{max}$ is equal to 10^{134}. Note, however, that $p_{L\,max}W_{max}X_{max}Y_{max} \cong p_{L\,max}$ since

$$10^{-(10^{11} - 134)} \cong 10^{-10^{11}}$$

The approximation holds because $134 \ll 10^{11}$.

When we encounter such small numbers as $p_{L\,max}$, no amount of ordinary manipulation or arguing about the age of the universe or the size of the system can suffice to make it plausible that such a fluctuation would have occurred in an equilibrium system. It is always possible to argue that any unique event would have occurred. This is outside the range of probabilistic considerations, and really, outside of science. We shall subsequently show that it is not necessary to invoke such arguments to explain biological organization. We may sum up by stating that on energy considerations alone, the possibility of a living cell occurring in an equilibrium ensemble is vanishingly small.

It is important to reiterate this point as a number of authors on the origin of life have missed the significance of vanishingly small probabilities. They have assumed that the final probability will be reasonably large by virtue of the size and age of the system. The previous paragraph shows that this is not so: calculable values of the probability of spontaneous origin are so low that the final probabilities are still vanishingly small.

The idea used in defining p_L may be generalized to give a measure of order that is applicable to abiotic systems as well as living systems. Consider any nonequilibrium system which can be defined by a set of macroscopic or microscopic properties. Then consider the same system isolated by rigid walls and allowed to equilibrate with a reservoir which is at the same kinetic temperature as the initial nonequilibrium system. The possible states of the nonequilibrium system must be represented in the set applicable to the equilibrium distribution. If we now define δ_{iP} as a Kronecker delta with a value 1 for microstates which have the desired properties of the original nonequilibrium system, and a value 0 for all other states, the probability of a member of the equilibrium ensemble having the properties is:

$$p_P = \sum_i p_i \, \delta_{iP} \qquad (1\text{-}13)$$

The smaller the value of p_P, the more ordered the system. This accords with intuitive notions of order in that equilibrium is the condition of maximum disorder consistent with the constraints. In measuring order, we compare systems of equal kinetic temperature. The less probable a system is in its isothermal equilibrium ensemble, the more ordered it is. In terms of classical statistical mechanics, the assertion is that ordered configurations of the system occupy regions of phase space far from the dense clusters characteristic of equilibrium in a canonical ensemble. In Chapter VI this concept will be reviewed in more detail.

Since the p_i are a normalized set of probabilities, p_P is always less than 1. If we choose the quantity $-\ln p_P$ as our measure of order, it will always be positive and will increase as p_P decreases, in accordance with our previous notions. By choosing this functional form, we also make contact with the formalism of information theory, since $-\ln_2 p_P$ is the amount of information we would have in knowing that a member of the equilibrium ensemble had the desired property of the initial non-equilibrium system.

In defining order, we could have chosen our ensembles in alternative ways. The original nonequilibrium system could have been adiabatically isolated at constant volume or isothermally and isobarically isolated. Each type of isolation leads to a different ensemble and corresponds to a different free energy function. The particular isolation conceptually employed is a matter of convenience, although the numerical measure of order depends on the particular isolation used.

While the expression $-\ln p_P$ is conceptually helpful as a measure of order, it suffers from the weakness that no direct experimental methods exist for arriving at this quantity. However, a specific example yields some clues as to the relationships between our order measure and thermodynamically measurable quantities. Assume that δ_{iP} is zero for all i except $i = j$; that is, the nonequilibrium system corresponds to only one state in the canonical ensemble. We may then write

$$
\begin{aligned}
p_P &= \frac{\exp(-\epsilon_j/kT)}{\sum \exp(-\epsilon_i/kT)} \\
&= \frac{\exp(-\epsilon_j/kT)}{Z} \qquad (1\text{-}14)
\end{aligned}
$$

where Z is the partition function of statistical mechanics, and

$$-\ln p_P = \frac{\epsilon_j}{kT} + \ln Z$$

$$= \frac{\epsilon_j}{kT} - \frac{A}{kT} \tag{1-15}$$

where $A = U - TS$ is the Helmholtz free energy. The internal energy and entropy are represented by U and S. The term ϵ_j may be regarded as the Helmholtz free energy of the nonequilibrium state since $\epsilon_j = U$ and $S = 0$, as only one state comprises the system. The quantity $-kT \ln p_P$ is thus the fluctuation in Helmholtz free energy between the nonequilibrium state and the equilibrium ensemble. The quantity $-\ln p_P$ is a ratio of stored energy (the difference in energy between the nonequilibrium state and the average energy of the equilibrium ensemble) to thermal energy which becomes a useful parameter in the description of order. The class of functions used to designate order in this way will be referred to as L functions.

The previous example is somewhat artificial in that the nonequilibrium situation is restricted to only one microstate, which constitutes a very overly restricted case except for systems very near to the absolute zero of temperature. The idea may be generalized by considering that the nonequilibrium state includes all microstates of the canonical ensemble of energy ϵ_l, where there are W' such microstates. We thus select the nonequilibrium configuration as a microcanonical ensemble of energy ϵ_l chosen from the canonical ensemble. We may then write:

$$p_P = \frac{W' \exp(-\epsilon_l/kT)}{Z} \tag{1-16}$$

and

$$-\ln p_P = \frac{(\epsilon_l - kT \ln W') - A}{kT} \tag{1-17}$$

The order measure is again the difference between the Helmholtz free energies of the equilibrium and nonequilibrium states divided by the thermal energy term kT.

Another example extends the concept of order functions a bit further. Suppose that our initial isolation of the nonequilibrium system was an adiabatic one at constant volume rather than an isothermal one at constant kinetic temperature. The ensemble corresponding to this isolation is microcanonical in which all states have equal energy and equal *a priori* probability. Suppose, now, that there are a total of W' possible states of the system and P of these possess the property of the initial nonequilibrium system. Then,

$$p_P = \frac{P}{W'} \tag{1-18}$$

$$-\ln p_P = -\ln P + \ln W' \tag{1-19}$$

We may recast this in thermodynamic form by noting that $k \ln W'$ is the Boltzmann expression for entropy in a microcanonical ensemble. If the initial temperature is T_i and the equilibrium temperature is T_f, then:

$$-\ln p_P = -\frac{T_i k \ln P}{kT_i} + \frac{T_f k \ln W'}{kT_f} \tag{1-20}$$

$$-\ln p_P = -\frac{T_i S_i}{kT_i} + \frac{T_f S_f}{kT_f} \tag{1-21}$$

If we designate $k \ln P$ as S_i, the effective entropy of the initial configuration, then $-\ln p_P$ is again the difference between two terms of the form of a configurational free energy divided by a thermal energy.

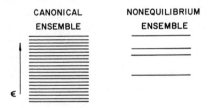

FIG. 1-2. Energy diagram indicating the possible energy states of members of the canonical ensemble and the more restrictive set of states characteristic of a particular nonequilibrium configuration. The nonequilibrium states are a subset of the larger set used in the equilibrium description.

We may now generalize and summarize the case for isothermal isolation. First, note that on page 8 we have indicated the possibility of defining a kinetic temperature for any system. We now assert that any nonequilibrium system can be completely described as a subset of states of the canonical ensemble having the same kinetic temperature, volume, and chemical composition as the nonequilibrium system. This is represented in Fig. 1-2. We can now pose the question: What is the probability of finding a member of the canonical ensemble in the particular nonequilibrium configuration of interest? This is clearly

$$p_P = \frac{\sum_l \exp(-\epsilon_l/kT)}{Z}$$

$$= \frac{\sum_i \exp(-\epsilon_i/kT)\,\delta_{iP}}{Z} \tag{1-22}$$

where the subscript l represents only those states that are members of the nonequilibrium subset. We can then define

$$Z_l = \sum_l \exp(-\epsilon_l/kT) \tag{1-23}$$

$$A_l = \sum p_l\epsilon_l + Tk \sum p_l \ln p_l \tag{1-24}$$

$$p_l = \frac{\exp(-\epsilon_l/kT)}{Z_l} \tag{1-25}$$

We may then write

$$L = -\ln p_P = \frac{A_l - A}{kT} \tag{1-26}$$

The order is represented by the change in Helmholtz free energy necessary to specify the nonequilibrium state divided by kT. At equilibrium, fluctuations of any appreciable magnitude are extremely rare. On the other hand, energy flow puts energy in the system and raises the probability of occurrence of certain nonequilibrium states.

In the preceding discussion, we have implicitly utilized the concept of a complete set of chemical equilibrium states. In thermodynamics we generally use states which are at equilibrium with respect to processes taking place on one time scale but which have not equilibrated with respect to processes taking place at much slower rates. In the general formalism discussed here and in subsequent chapters on the evolution of biological systems, all chemical processes must be considered. If we start out, for example, with a container of pure methane, the final equilibrium systems would include all possible compounds of hydrogen and carbon. This type of complete chemical equilibrium is, of course, much more difficult to deal with than the more restricted equilibria which are usually treated. The ensembles are considerably more generalized than those usually encountered in statistical mechanics. This more general theory involves all the difficulties of statistical treatment of pure species and simple mixtures, plus a second averaging over all possible molecular species. In subsequent chapters, particularly Chapter III, we will be concerned with attempts to treat this more general case.

We now turn our attention to the relation between ordering processes and classical thermodynamics. The second law of thermodynamics demands that an increase of entropy accompany any spontaneous process. The energy flux thesis speaks of the ordering of the intermediate system. Ordering is usually thought to be associated with an entropy decrease so that we must investigate the relation between the energy flux principle and the second law.

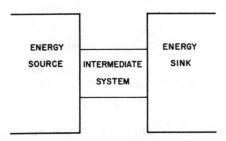

FIG. 1-3. Schematic representation of a generalized energy flow system showing the three essential features: an energy source, an energy sink, and an intermediate system through which the energy flows.

If we refer to Fig. 1-3, we see a diagram of the generalized system involved in energy flow considerations. The system may be split into two parts, the source–sink (s) and the intermediate system (i). The requirement of the second law is that

$$dS_s + dS_i \geqslant 0 \tag{1-27}$$

The flow of energy from a source to a sink will always lead to an entropy increase in the source–sink system.

$$dS_s > 0 \tag{1-28}$$

The only restriction placed on dS_i by the second law is:

$$-dS_i \leqslant dS_s \tag{1-29}$$

The entropy of the intermediate system may, therefore, decrease in an energy flow process. In Chapter II, we will discuss a different view of this problem from the approach of local entropy production.

We may make the preceding idea more concrete by considering a model system which involves such an entropy decrease. For the source and sink consider two infinite isothermal reservoirs of temperature T_1 and T_2 where $T_1 > T_2$.

The intermediate system will consist of a Carnot engine driving a piston which is reversibly compressing M moles of perfect gas, which is in contact with the lower temperature reservoir. In driving the engine around one complete cycle, an amount of heat Q_1 is taken from the reservoir by the Carnot engine, an amount Q_2 is given up to the sink, and an amount of work ΔW is done on the gas.

$$\Delta W = Q_1 - Q_2 \qquad (1\text{-}30)$$

In compressing the gas,

$$\Delta W = -\int_{V_1}^{V_2} p\, dV = MRT_2 \ln \frac{V_1}{V_2} \qquad (1\text{-}31)$$

Since the internal energy is a function of temperature only,

$$\Delta U = Q_3 - \Delta W \qquad (1\text{-}32)$$

The amount of heat given to the reservoir Q_3 is equal to the amount of work done. The entropy change of the source–sink system is:

$$\Delta S_s = -\frac{Q_1}{T_1} + \frac{Q_2}{T_2} + \frac{Q_3}{T_2} = \frac{Q_3}{T_2} \qquad (1\text{-}33)$$

since $\Delta S = 0$ for one complete cycle of the Carnot engine, and is equal to $-(Q_1/T_1) + (Q_2/T_2)$. For the gas in the piston,

$$\Delta S_i = MR \ln \frac{V_2}{V_1} = -\frac{Q_3}{T_2} \qquad (1\text{-}34)$$

The total entropy change $\Delta S_s + \Delta S_i$ is zero, while the intermediate system is undergoing an entropy decrease of Q_3/T_2.

Thus, we have shown that a spontaneous process may lead to a local entropy decrease in an intermediate system between a source and a sink. While the energy flow thesis is not derivable from the second law of thermodynamics, it does not contradict this principle.

The previous discussion can be generalized by using the work principle of Brønsted (*14*). Katchalsky and Curran (*4*) give this statement of the principle: "... the over-all work ΔW performed by a system is the sum of contributions due to transport of extensive quantities ΔK_i across a difference of conjugated potentials $\mathscr{P}_i(1) - \mathscr{P}_i(2)$

$$\Delta W = \sum_{i=1}^{k} (\mathscr{P}_i(1) - \mathscr{P}_i(2)) \Delta K_i \qquad (1\text{-}35)$$

in which, for example, $\mathscr{P}_i(1) - \mathscr{P}_i(2)$ may be $T_1 - T_2$, $\mu_1 - \mu_2$, or $\Psi_1 - \Psi_2$ and the ΔK_i will be ΔS, Δn, or Δe, respectively." Here T is temperature, μ is chemical potential, Ψ is electrical potential, n is mole number, and e is electrical charge.

The $\mathscr{P}_i(1)$ and $\mathscr{P}_i(2)$ can be regarded as characteristic of the source and sink. The transport of extensive quantities ΔK_i is always accompanied by the flow of energy from source to sink. The reversible flow of energy from source to sink across an intermediate system can always give rise to a work term ΔW. Part of this can always be used to order the system. Hence, the generalized flow of energy from source to sink can always lead to ordering of the intermediate system within the restrictions of the second law of thermodynamics.

In terms of our present viewpoint, it is instructive to examine a discussion of thermodynamics and life by Erwin Schrödinger (15). The noted physicist raised the point: "How would we express in terms of the statistical theory the marvelous faculty of a living organism, by which it delays the decay into thermodyanmical equilibrium (death)? We said before: 'It feeds upon negative entropy,' attracting, as it were, a stream of negative entropy upon itself, to compensate the entropy increase it produces by living and thus to maintain itself on a stationary and fairly low entropy level."

We may now reword the Schrödinger argument in the following terms. An isolated organism will be subject to a series of processes tending toward equilibrium. In statistical terms, it will tend to move from the very improbable state that it is in to one of the very probable states associated with the equilibrium ensemble. In order to prevent this drift toward equilibrium, it is constantly necessary to perform work to move the system back into the improbable state that it is drifting out of. An isolated system, however, cannot do steady work. The necessary condition for this is that the system be connected with a source and a sink and the work be associated with a flow of energy from source to sink. This flow will be an exentropic process in terms of the external world, i.e., the source and sink. When Schrödinger says that the organism feeds on negentropy, he means simply that its existence depends upon increasing the entropy of the rest of the universe.

While Schrödinger rather poetically worded his argument in terms of negentropy, in the present analysis we found it more useful to concentrate on the energy aspect of the argument. For nonequilibrium systems, it is often difficult to define entropy, while energy and energy flow are often more accessible quantities.

Interestingly, an idea very similar to Schrödinger's was put forward by Otto Meyerhof (*16*). In a later series of lectures (*17*) he stated, "I advanced some time ago the general hypothesis that in consequence of the fluid state of the protoplasm and the instability of the cell-stuffs, voluntary events of physical and chiefly of chemical nature are going on continuously which aim at a balance of the existing potentials of energy. Since life requires the continuation of these potentials of energy, work must be performed continuously for the prevention or reversion of these spontaneous changes." Again, we note that maintaining order requires continuous work, which can be supplied only by the flow of energy from a source to a sink.

Finally, we may note that the importance of energy flux in biology was grasped many years ago by the physicist Percy Bridgeman (*1*) whose penetrating analysis of thermodynamics included the remark, "For instance, the environment of most living things is a stream of radiation from the sun to the earth, from which they extract energy which is used in the 'organization' of the environment. The stream itself is a factor with 'order' in the determining conditions."

References

1. P. W. Bridgeman, "The Nature of Thermodynamics." Harvard Univ. Press, Cambridge, Massachusetts, 1941.
2. I. Prigogine, "Introduction to the Thermodynamics of Irreversible Processes." C. C. Thomas, Springfield, Illinois, 1955.
3. S. R. de Groot and P. Mazur, "Non-Equilibrium Thermodynamics." North-Holland, Amsterdam and Wiley, New York, 1962.
4. A. Katchalsky and P. F. Curran, "Nonequilibrium Thermodynamics in Biophysics." Harvard Univ. Press, Cambridge, Massachusetts, 1965.
5. D. M. Gates, "Energy Exchange in the Biosphere." Harper, New York, 1962.
6. T. Hill, "An Introduction to Statistical Thermodynamics." Addison-Wesley, Reading, Massachusetts, 1960.
7. H. B. Callen, "Thermodynamics." Wiley, New York, 1960.
8. J. C. Slater, "Introduction to Chemical Physics." McGraw-Hill, New York, 1939.
9. S. Chapman and T. G. Cowling, "The Mathematical Theory of Non-Uniform Gases." Cambridge Univ. Press, London and New York, 1939.
10. E. Schrödinger, "Statistical Thermodynamics." Cambridge Univ. Press, London and New York, 1957.
11. W. Elsasser, "Atom and Organism." Princeton Univ. Press, Princeton, New Jersey, 1966.
12. E. T. Jaynes, *Phys. Rev.* **106**, 620 (1957).
13. S. Glasstone, K. J. Laidler, and H. Eyring, "The Theory of Rate Processes." McGraw-Hill, New York, 1941.
14. J. N. Brønsted, "Principles and Problems in Energetics." Wiley (Interscience), New York, 1955.

15. E. Schrödinger, "What Is Life?" Cambridge Univ. Press, London and New York, 1945.
16. O. Meyerhof, "Zur Energetik der Zellvorgaenge." Vandenhoek and Ruprecht, Goettingen, 1913.
17. O. Meyerhof, "Chemical Dynamics of Life Phenomena." Lippincott, Philadelphia, Pennsylvania, 1924.

II

The Evolution of Molecular Order in Physical Systems

Tsze-lû asked about energy.
The Master said, "Do you mean the energy of the South,
the energy of the North, or the energy which you should
cultivate yourself?
"To show forbearance and gentleness in teaching others; and
not to revenge unreasonable conduct:—this is the energy of
Southern regions, and the good man makes it his study.
"To lie under arms; and meet death without regret;—this is
energy of Northern regions, and the forceful make it their
study.
"Therefore, the superior man cultivates a friendly harmony,
without being weak.—How firm is he in his energy! He
stands erect in the middle, without inclining to either
side.—How firm is he in his energy! When good principles
prevail in the government of his country, he does not change
from what he was in retirement.—How firm is he in his energy!
When bad principles prevail in the country, he maintains his
course to death without changing.—How firm is he in his
energy!"

Confucius

In this chapter, we shall demonstrate in very general ways how molecular order arises in systems undergoing energy flow. We shall examine a number of model systems and prove a theorem relating to the existence of cycles in steady state systems. In discussing a photosynthetic example of the cycling theorem, we make contact with biochemistry. The relationship of the general theory to specific organic compounds and biochemical reactions will be continued and expanded in Chapter III. The model systems are intended to illustrate how energy flow can lead to molecular organization in rather generalized systems.

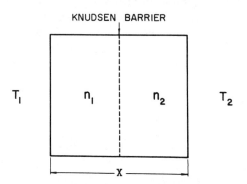

FIG. 2-1. Two chambers connected by a Knudsen barrier which is characterized by pore diameters small in comparison with the mean free path of the molecules. The left side is at a temperature T_1 and the right side at temperature T_2. The steady state flow of heat leads to a concentration difference on the two sides of the barrier.

The first model system we will deal with consists of a perfect gas between two infinite plane isothermal reservoirs at temperatures T_1 and T_2 ($T_1 > T_2$). In the steady state, there will be a constant flow of heat dQ/dt from the hotter of the two reservoirs to the colder. The steady state will be characterized by two functions: $n(x)$, the density of atoms as a function of position between the two reservoirs and $T(x)$, the temperature as a function of position. The exact solution of $n(x)$ and $T(x)$ is a somewhat complex problem in kinetic theory and is discussed in more detail in Appendix II.

An approximate method exists which permits simplified calculations in problems of this type yet preserves the general features of organization that we wish to discuss. Midway between the two reservoirs place a Knudsen barrier, a structure with pores having a diameter small compared with the mean free path of the gas molecules. The idealized barrier is itself adiabatic and the only allowable flow of energy across the barrier is mediated by the gas molecules in the pores of the barrier. We now maintain perfect mixing on each side of the barrier so that we can assign a well-defined temperature and molecular density to each side T_1, n_1, T_2, n_2. This condition will be approximately maintained without external mixing if the flows across the barrier are sufficiently small so that an approximate uniform state can be established on each side. The entire temperature gradient will then be across the barrier.

The system of interest will now consist of two reservoirs separated by a distance X and bounding an intermediate system consisting of a box of area Φ and thickness X with a Knudsen barrier at the point $X/2$. The sides of the box not in contact with the reservoir are adiabatic and the box contains $\Psi\Phi X$ atoms of a perfect gas. The main features are shown in Fig. 2-1. The Knudsen barrier problem has been solved (1), and the steady state is found to be:

$$n_1\sqrt{T_1} = n_2\sqrt{T_2} \qquad (2\text{-}1)$$

where

$$\frac{n_1\Phi X}{2} + \frac{n_2\Phi X}{2} = \Psi\Phi X \qquad (2\text{-}2)$$

Equation (2-1) is the kinetic theory solution to the problem, while Eq. (2-2) is an expression of conservation of gas molecules. The number densities then become:

$$n_1 = \frac{2\Psi\sqrt{T_2}}{\sqrt{T_1} + \sqrt{T_2}}$$
$$\qquad (2\text{-}3)$$
$$n_2 = \frac{2\Psi\sqrt{T_1}}{\sqrt{T_1} + \sqrt{T_2}}$$

The flow of energy through the system thus leads to a concentration difference on the two sides of the barrier. This order is clearly maintained by the energy flux: if we were to isolate the intermediate system by placing adiabatic walls between it and the reservoir, the systems would come to an equilibrium state in which $n_1 = n_2$.

The steady state solution represents a very unlikely fluctuation of the equilibrium system and, consequently, an ordered system by the criteria established in Chapter I. The order arises as a result of the energy flow. It should be noted that the Knudsen barrier is a computational device and does not give rise to the order. In Fig. 2-2 we examine the system with and without the barrier. In the absence of the barrier we would still have a nonuniform system maintained in the ordered state by energy flow as is shown in Appendix II.

For the Knudsen barrier model we can calculate the order measure in the following way. We may adiabatically isolate the entire system and allow it to equilibrate, in which case the final temperature can be shown

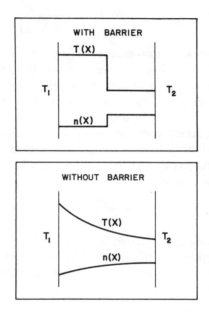

FIG. 2-2.   Concentration and temperature profiles for a gas between two temperature reservoirs at temperatures T_1 and T_2. At the top, the distribution is represented with a Knudsen barrier midway between the reservoirs. At the bottom, the distribution is shown without the barrier. The bottom case is analyzed in Appendix II.

to be $T_3 = (T_1 T_2)^{1/2}$. We may then compare the entropy of the final system with that of the initial system in accordance with Eqs. (1-20) and (1-21). This utilizes the microcanonical ensemble to measure order. The entropy of a perfect gas is given (2) by:

$$S = \Psi k \ln\left[\left(\frac{2\pi m k T}{h^2}\right)^{3/2}\left(\frac{Ve}{\Psi}\right)^{5/2}\right]$$ (2-4)

The order function is then given by:

$$L = -\ln p_P = S_f - S_i$$ (2-5)

$$L = \Psi\Phi Xk\left[\ln\left(\frac{T_3^{3/2}}{\Psi}\right)\right.$$

$$-\frac{\sqrt{T_2}}{\sqrt{T_1}+\sqrt{T_2}}\ln\left(\frac{T_1^{3/2}}{n_1}\right)$$

$$\left.-\frac{\sqrt{T_1}}{\sqrt{T_1}+\sqrt{T_2}}\ln\left(\frac{T_2^{3/2}}{n_2}\right)\right] \tag{2-6}$$

This model may seem remote from biology and is in some respects. It is, however, the simplest example of two important ideas: (a) that energy flow alone can give rise to order in a system and (b) that continued energy flow is necessary to maintain order once it has been achieved.

An additional feature may now be added to the Knudsen barrier model which will demonstrate some of the further possibilities of organization in energy flow systems. Starting with the previous model system, replace the perfect gas by a perfect gas species which can undergo an isomerization reaction of the form

$$A \underset{k_2(T)}{\overset{k_1(T)}{\rightleftharpoons}} B$$

The system is now characterized by four concentration values $[A_1]$, $[B_1]$, $[A_2]$, $[B_2]$ where the subscript 1 refers to values on the left-hand side of the barrier and the subscript 2 refers to the right-hand side. The behavior of the system may now be represented by the equations:

$$\frac{d[A_1]}{dt} = -k_1(T_1)[A_1] + k_2(T_1)[B_1]$$
$$-\alpha\sqrt{T_1}[A_1] + \alpha\sqrt{T_2}[A_2] \tag{2-7}$$

$$\frac{d[B_1]}{dt} = k_1(T_1)[A_1] - k_2(T_1)[B_1]$$
$$-\alpha\sqrt{T_1}[B_1] + \alpha\sqrt{T_2}[B_2] \tag{2-8}$$

$$\frac{d[A_2]}{dt} = -k_1(T_2)[A_2] + k_2(T_2)[B_2]$$
$$+\alpha\sqrt{T_1}[A_1] - \alpha\sqrt{T_2}[A_2] \tag{2-9}$$

$$[A_1] + [B_1] + [A_2] + [B_2] = 2\Psi \tag{2-10}$$

The quantity α is a geometric constant characteristic of the barrier. The α terms represent the flow of material across the barrier. The dependence of the flow term on $\sqrt{T}$ reflects the fact that the transport is dependent on the average velocity of the molecules. In the steady state the concentrations will not vary with time and the derivatives $(d[A_1]/dt)$, $(d[B_1]/dt)$, $(d[A_2]/dt)$, $(d[B_2]/dt)$ are all equal to zero. Equations (2-7) through (2-10) can then be solved for $[A_1]$, $[A_2]$, $[B_1]$, $[B_2]$, yielding long but straightforward expressions. Rather than writing down the detailed solutions, we will prove a number of general propositions.

(1) *Chemical equilibrium solutions cannot obtain.* The equilibrium solution on the left-hand side would be:

$$\frac{[B_1]}{[A_1]} = \frac{k_1(T_1)}{k_2(T_1)} = K(T_1) \qquad (2\text{-}11)$$

where $K(T_1)$ is the equilibrium constant for the reaction. If we assume this solution and substitute into the steady state form of Eqs. (2-7) and (2-9), the following result is obtained:

$$\frac{[B_2]}{[A_2]} = \frac{k_1(T_2)}{k_2(T_2)} = K(T_2) \qquad (2\text{-}12)$$

Equilibrium on the left-hand side implies equilibrium on the right-hand side. On the other hand, substituting Eq. (2-10) into (2-7) and (2-8) and dividing (2-8) by (2-7) yields

$$\frac{[B_1]}{[A_1]} = \frac{[B_2]}{[A_2]} \qquad (2\text{-}13)$$

This implies

$$K(T_1) = K(T_2) \qquad (2\text{-}14)$$

Equation (2-14) states that the equilibrium constant is temperature independent. This cannot in general be true, it will only be the case when the enthalpy change of the reaction is zero since

$$K = \exp\left[-\left(\frac{\Delta H}{RT} - \frac{\Delta S}{R}\right)\right].$$

The equilibrium solutions cannot obtain. Thus, if we assume an equilibrium ratio of reactants and products, we are led to a false statement about the equilibrium constant. The assumption must be false and in the steady state case we are studying, equilibrium ratios cannot obtain on either side of the Knudsen barrier. The meaning of this type of result as applied to biology is that compounds will occur in steady states at concentrations different from the calculated equilibrium concentrations at the steady state temperature. The model system we are discussing indicates that in certain energy flow situations, nonequilibrium concentrations will be the expected behavior.

(2) *There is a cycle of substances A and B in the system.* From adding Eqs. (2-7) and (2-8) we note that the flow of A plus the flow of B across the barrier is zero. Thus, the flow of A is equal and opposite to the flow of B. From the previous case, we know that

$$k_1(T_1)[A_1] - k_2(T_1)[B_1] \neq 0 \qquad (2\text{-}15)$$

hence, the flow of A, which is

$$-\alpha\sqrt{T_1}[A_1] + \alpha\sqrt{T_2}[A_2]$$

is also nonzero [see Eq. (2-7)]. Thus, there is a finite flow of A in one direction and an equal and opposite flow of species B. This constitutes a cycle of material within the system. In biological studies, cycles take on great importance so that the physical origin of this type of behavior merits further study and will be subsequently discussed.

(3) By adding Eqs. (2-7) and (2-8), we can further note that

$$\sqrt{T_1}([A_1] + [B_1]) = \sqrt{T_2}([A_2] + [B_2])$$

As already noted, the net flow of matter from left to right is equal and opposite to the flow from right to left.

We may now sum up the clues that are provided by the simple model system we have been studying.

(*a*) The flow of heat from sources to sinks can lead to an internal organization of the system.

(*b*) Chemical equilibrium does not obtain in the steady state in the model system discussed.

(*c*) The flow of heat can lead to the formation of cyclic flows of material in the intermediate system.

The degree of organization in the systems we are studying may seem extremely simple and remote from biology as exemplified by the elaborate terrestrial biochemistry. However, our object at this point is simply to show that molecular organization is, in principle, a necessary consequence of energy flow.

The simple two-reservoir systems we have been studying can show extremely complex behavior if we allow a more elaborate series of chemical reactions to occur in the intermediate vessel. Assume that we start with a container of H_2O, CO_2, and N_2 with a preponderance of H_2O and allow the two reservoirs to be at 2000°C and 0°C. At the cold reservoir water will condense, while at the hot reservoir a wide variety of chemical reactions will take place, giving rise to free radicals and a number of organic compounds. These high energy molecules will have a finite probability of diffusing to the liquid phase where a number of them will go into solution. An elaborate series of chemical reactions will also take place in the liquid. As the system ages, a high concentration of organic molecules will build up in the liquid phase and it is even conceivable that another phase will form. An extremely complicated system will arise as a result of the energy flow which is required for maintenance of the improbable state. If we isolate the system from the two reservoirs by adiabatic walls, it will eventually deteriorate to a uniform system containing primarily H_2O, CO_2, and N_2 (equilibrium might take a very long time although the initial disruption will probably occur rapidly). An extremely simple set of boundary conditions can lead to a steady state of enormous molecular complexity.

We will next adopt a very general point of view to consider a theorem on the existence of cycles in steady state systems. We have already encountered a cycle in the case of a Knudsen barrier and an isomerization reaction. In this case, the cycle consisted of the net flow of species A in one direction, its conversion to B, and the equal net flow of B in the opposite direction. We wish to show that cycling behavior is a general property of steady states maintained by energy flux. In the general theorem, we will at first restrict ourselves to homogeneous systems.

Since the word *cycle* has a number of meanings, we will first make an aside to indicate in a more precise way the kind of cycle that is being referred to. The example we choose was used by Onsager in his original paper on irreversible thermodynamics (3, 4). For illustrative purposes, consider a vat in contact with an isothermal reservoir of temperature T. In the vat consider species A, B, and C which react according to the reaction scheme

$$
\begin{array}{c}
A \\
k_5 \diagup\!\!\diagup k_6 \quad k_2 \diagdown\!\!\diagdown k_1 \\
C \;\underset{k_3}{\overset{k_4}{\rightleftharpoons}}\; B
\end{array}
$$

As the system comes to equilibrium, the following relations hold:

$$
\begin{aligned}
k_1[A] &= k_2[B] \\
k_3[B] &= k_4[C] \\
k_5[C] &= k_6[A]
\end{aligned}
\tag{2-16}
$$

where the k's are rate constants and the brackets indicate concentrations. These equations follow from the principle of microscopic reversibility which states that at equilibrium, each process must have the same probability as the reverse process. Thus, at equilibrium there is no net flow around the system since the forward and back reaction are in detailed balance.* We may now introduce the condition that the total amount of material in the vat is constant,

$$[A] + [B] + [C] = M \qquad (2\text{-}17)$$

and then solve for the concentrations

$$A_{eq} = \frac{k_2 k_4 M}{k'}$$

$$B_{eq} = \frac{k_1 k_4 M}{k'} \qquad (2\text{-}18)$$

$$C_{eq} = \frac{k_1 k_3 M}{k'}$$

$$k' = k_2 k_4 + k_1 k_4 + k_1 k_3 \qquad (2\text{-}19)$$

We could have also determined the equilibrium concentrations directly from thermodynamics by noting

$$A_{eq} = \frac{M}{1 + \exp(-\Delta F_{AB}/RT) + \exp(-\Delta F_{AC}/RT)}$$

$$B_{eq} = \frac{M \exp(-\Delta F_{AB}/RT)}{1 + \exp(-\Delta F_{AB}/RT) + \exp(-\Delta F_{AC}/RT)} \qquad (2\text{-}20)$$

$$C_{eq} = \frac{M \exp(-\Delta F_{AC}/RT)}{1 + \exp(-\Delta F_{AB}/RT) + \exp(-\Delta F_{AC}/RT)}$$

* It is worthwhile at this point to take note of Onsager's discussion of this concept (3). He wrote, "Barring certain exceptional cases which can readily be recognized and sorted out, the dynamical laws of familiar conservative systems are always reversible, that means: if the velocities of all the particles present are reversed simultaneously the particles will retrace their former paths, reversing the entire succession of configurations. We like to think that the dynamical laws which govern the world of atoms are also reversible. The information that we have about the atom affords considerable support for this belief of ours, and we have no serious counter-indications, if any. If the dynamical laws of an isolated molecular system are reversible the kinetic theory requires that in the long run every type of motion must occur just as often as its reverse, because the congruence of the two types of motion makes them *apriori* equivalent. This implies that if we wait a long time so as to make sure of thermodynamic equilibrium, in the end every type of motion is just as likely to occur as its reverse. One consequence of this principle of dynamical reversibility is the condition that when a molecule changes a certain number of times per second from the configuration A to the configuration B the direct reverse transition B → A must take place equally often, ..."

These three equations (2-20) are the only requirements of thermo-dynamics. The rate-balance equations are a separate requirement of "the principal of microscopic reversibility." Thus, in principle, we could have the same final concentration by maintaining a net flow of material around the system. The steady state condition would then require that

$$k_1[A] - k_2[B] = k_3[B] - k_4[C] = k_5[C] - k_6[A] = \mathscr{F} \qquad (2\text{-}21)$$

where $\mathscr{F}$ is the flow, the rate at which the material is cycling around the system. It is precisely this flow of material around a closed loop that we wish to designate as a cycle for purposes of the theorem that follows.

The purpose of the analysis is then to demonstrate that the existence of material cycles is characteristic of any physical system that represents a steady state brought about by the flow of energy from a high potential source to a low potential sink (5). To construct a formal system, we first consider the particular case where the energy flows into the system as electromagnetic energy and flows out as heat. We will then generalize this result to other energy flow systems, including the case where energy flux is linked to the flow of chemical species from a high chemical potential to a low chemical potential.

Consider a canonical ensemble of systems at equilibrium. The possible states of a system are each characterized by energy ϵ_i and designated by subscript i. The equilibrium description of the system consists of a set of numbers f_i designating the fraction of systems in the ith state. Any individual system is not static and is constantly changing state. Designate by t_{ij} the transition probability that a system in state i will change to state j in unit time. Then the principle of dynamic reversibility, or detailed balance (3, 4), requires that

$$f_i t_{ij} = f_j t_{ji} \qquad (2\text{-}22)$$

Next, consider the same ensemble which is in contact with an infinite isothermal reservoir but is irradiated with a.constant flux of electro-magnetic radiation such that there is a net absorption of radiation by the system. The steady state will be characterized by a flow of heat to the reservoir equal to the flow of electromagnetic energy into the system.

When the system finally achieves the steady state, it will be charac-terized by a new set of occupation numbers and transition probabilities f_i' and t_{ij}'. The new transition probabilities will include the initial type of random thermal transitions as well as radiation-induced transitions. We shall now show that there are some pairs of states i and j for which the relation given in Eq. (2-23) cannot hold,

$$f_i' t_{ij}' = f_j' t_{ji}' \qquad (2\text{-}23)$$

First, assume that Eq. (2-23) holds for all pairs of states. This means that for every transition involving the absorption of radiation by the system, a reverse transition will exist in which the system will radiate a photon. There will then be no net absorption of electromagnetic energy by the system. This, however, contradicts our assumption that the system absorbs radiant energy; hence, we must conclude that there are pairs of states for which relation (2-23) does not hold. However, in the steady state all the f_i' terms are time independent. Hence, we note that

$$\frac{df_i'}{dt} = 0 = \sum_{ij} (f_i' t_{ij}' - f_j' t_{ji}') \qquad (2\text{-}24)$$

For some f_i' terms we have established that $f_i' t_{ij}' - f_j' t_{ji}'$ must be non-zero. Other pairs must then also be non-zero. That is, members of the ensemble must leave certain states by one path and return by other paths. Formally, this constitutes a cycle, and leads to a statement that we shall later designate as the "cycling theorem."

The reasoning used in the derivation just presented bears some relation to Einstein's derivation of the black body radiation law and may be examined in more detail from that point of view. Note first that in the complete representation of states, transitions that are involved in the emission and absorption of radiation cannot occur in one step by any other process. The other available processes all involve collisions. The intermediates in the collision processes are activated complexes which are microstates in their own right in a complete representation. Hence, alternative pathways from i to j must involve at least two steps and are not included for the radiation transitions in Eq. (2-23). This point of view is at variance with the procedures in Eqs. (1-7) through (1-11). In that instance we took a coarser grained point of view of the situation and concerned ourselves only with concentrations rather than the details of the flows around the system. We therefore grouped together the two types of transitions which must now be separated in our more detailed analysis. The transitions involving radiation will, however, occur in the equilibrium state since thermal equilibrium also includes a black body radiation field. The requirements of radiation equilibrium are that each forward transition occurs with the same frequency as its inverse transition. The net absorption of electromagnetic energy must unbalance this condition, for if the forward and back steps took place with equal frequency for a given wavelength, as many photons would be emitted as absorbed and no overall absorption would occur.

In our analysis we have not specifically included the induced emission term of Einstein, as we have not been concerned about the detailed nature of the t'_{ij}. These details are not significant in the previous proof as we only require the unbalance condition for the cycling theorem and do not require a numerical estimate of the degree of unbalance. Such a requirement would demand a detailed kinetic analysis including the kinetics of absorption and emission of radiation. We may now turn to a general statement of the cycling theorem.

Theorem. *In steady state systems, the flow of energy through the system from a source to a sink will lead to at least one cycle in the system.*

The above example is a special case, but it can be generalized by the realization that the flow of energy into the system by any means will always be accompanied by a transition $i \rightarrow j$ where $\epsilon_j > \epsilon_i$.

For the transitions involved in energy flow into the system, detailed balance cannot obtain because it is contrary to the net flow of energy. The breakdown of detailed balance at any point leads to cycling in the steady state. The same argument could have been applied to those transitions whereby energy leaves the system and flows into the sink.

The flow of energy can be accompanied by the flow of matter. Thus, the steady state flow of compounds of high chemical potential into a system and low chemical potential out of the system will also lead to cycling. If the induced states j represent a different distribution of chemical compounds than the i states, the cycling will represent a chemical flow of matter around the systems.

The theorem as derived is very general and refers to states of the system as quantum mechanical states. There are no restrictions as to the complexity of the system. Thus, if our theorem were applied to pure argon gas, the cycling would be between various excited states of argon atoms. In order for the theorem to be biochemically interesting, the states must be chemically distinguishable. If the incoming photons cause electronic transitions leading to chemical rearrangements in the appropriate system of atoms, this condition will be met. Two simple examples are now presented.

Example I.   Consider a closed isothermal vat containing compounds

A, B, and C with the reaction scheme as previously used on page 29. At equilibrium,

$$[A]k_1 = [B]k_2$$
$$[B]k_3 = [C]k_4 \qquad (2\text{-}25)$$
$$[C]k_5 = [A]k_6$$

If we now irradiate the vat with monochromatic radiation of frequency ν such that the following photochemical reaction occurs,

$$A + h\nu \rightarrow B \qquad (2\text{-}26)$$

then a cycle will take place and in the steady state, there will be a net flow of material around the cycle from A to B to C to A.

Example II. Consider the vat from example I in contact, through a semipermeable membrane, with a reservoir of constant chemical potentials for substances D and E where $\mu_D > \mu_E$. Also, consider the membrane impermeable to A, B, and C. Next, consider the following reaction scheme:

$$A + D \rightleftharpoons B + E \qquad (2\text{-}27)$$

Material will now cycle around the system from A to B to C to A.

In the steady state, there will be a constant flow of D into the system and a flow of E out of the system. A net amount of energy $\Delta H = H_E - H_D$ will be transferred to the intermediate system per mole of reaction. Since energy cannot accumulate in the intermediate system in the steady state, there is a net flow of heat $-\Delta H$ to the isothermal reservoir. Thus, high energy compounds flow in and low energy compounds and heat flow out; energy flow is maintained and cycles occur in the intermediate system.

Biology, as already noted, is characterized by cycles in systems which are approaching steady states of intermediate stability. The theorem discussed earlier indicates that such cycles are a general consequence of the physics of systems undergoing energy flux and need not be introduced as special biological phenomena.

It will be instructive at this point to examine example I in some detail. First, this treatment will point up the difficulties that will be encountered in a brute force kinetic analysis of chemical networks of any degree of complexity. Second, a number of features of energy flow organization will emerge from this case. Third, this system represents the most primitive type of photosynthetic cycle and will be useful in making contact between theory and problems of terrestrial energy balance.

We start by representing our system diagrammatically on an energy level diagram and an energy plot as used in absolute reaction rate theory. This is shown in Fig. 2-3. Next, consider an actual physical setup shown in Fig. 2-4 consisting of a rectangular vat in contact with an infinite isothermal reservoir of temperature T. One side of the vat is a window

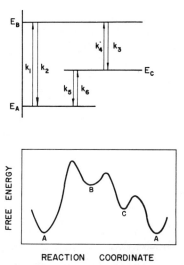

FIG. 2-3. Energy diagram of model system used to demonstrate some of the fundamental features of a photosynthetic cycle. A, B, and C are isomers which may undergo interconversion reactions. In the case discussed in the text, there is a photochemical transition from A to B.

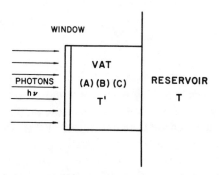

FIG. 2-4. Diagram of the model system used to demonstrate photosynthetic cycles. Electromagnetic energy enters the system through the window, photochemical reactions take place in the vat, and heat flows to the reservoir.

through which a flux of photons per unit area G_0 is maintained. The vat has a depth l and the wavelength of the photons is determined by:

$$hv = E_B - E_A \tag{2-28}$$

The extinction coefficients γ_C and γ_B are zero and γ_A is finite. Uniform mixing is maintained in the system. The following equations describe the behavior of the system:

$$k_1[A] + \frac{G_0}{l}[1 - \exp(-\gamma_A l[A])] - k_2[B] = \mathscr{F}_{AB} \tag{2-29}$$

$$k_3[B] - k_4[C] = \mathscr{F}_{BC} \tag{2-30}$$

$$k_5[C] - k_6[A] = \mathscr{F}_{CA} \tag{2-31}$$

where $G_0[1 - \exp(-\gamma_A l[A])]$ is the amount of energy absorbed by the Beer–Lambert law and the $\mathscr{F}_{ij}$ terms are flows of material from isomer i to isomer j per unit volume. We also note that

$$a(T' - T) = \mathscr{F}_E \tag{2-32}$$

where T' is the steady state temperature of the system and a is the thermal transfer coefficient per unit area.

$$[A] + [B] + [C] = M \tag{2-33}$$

where $\mathscr{F}_E$ is the energy flux per unit area and M is the total amount of material in the system. The steady state is characterized by a balanced flow around the network,

$$\mathscr{F}_{AB} = \mathscr{F}_{BC} = \mathscr{F}_{CA} \tag{2-34}$$

In addition an energy balance must obtain,

$$hvG_0[1 - \exp(-\gamma_A l[A])] = a(T' - T) \tag{2-35}$$

For the equilibrium condition, G_0 is zero and $\mathscr{F}_{AB}$, $\mathscr{F}_{BC}$, and $\mathscr{F}_{CA}$ are all zero. This leads to Eqs. (2-18) through (2-20). Cyclic elimination of the variables leads to

$$k_1 k_3 k_5 = k_2 k_4 k_6 \tag{2-36}$$

In general, the existence of cycles means that the reaction rate constants are not all independent, since the reaction rates are functionally related to the equilibrium constants and the free energy changes around a closed loop must add up to zero. The steady state equations in the photon flux case become:

$$k_1[A] - (k_2 + k_3)[B] + k_4[C] = -\frac{G_0}{l}[1 - \exp(-\gamma_A l[A])] \tag{2-37}$$

$$k_6[A] + k_3[B] - (k_4 + k_5)[C] = 0 \tag{2-38}$$

which along with Eqs. (2-32) and (2-33) completely define the problem. Because of the exponentials, the set of equations cannot generally be solved analytically. In this regard we might note that the k's are themselves exponential functions of T. One special case can, however, be handled—where $\gamma_A l[A] \gg 1$ and $G_0[1 - \exp(-\gamma_A l[A])] = G_0$—that is, when all the incoming radiant energy is absorbed. For this condition, we can solve directly for T' which becomes $T + (h\nu G_0/a)$. This value may then be substituted into the equations for the rate constants. We may then employ determinants and write down the solutions of the form

$$[A] = \frac{\begin{vmatrix} \left(\dfrac{-G_0}{l}\right) & -(k_2 + k_3) & k_4 \\ 0 & k_3 & -(k_4 + k_5) \\ M & 1 & 1 \end{vmatrix}}{\begin{vmatrix} k_1 & -(k_2 + k_3) & k_4 \\ k_6 & k_3 & -(k_4 + k_5) \\ 1 & 1 & 1 \end{vmatrix}} \quad (2\text{-}39)$$

We can immediately write down the full solutions by evaluating the appropriate determinants. It can be shown that as G_0 goes to zero, [A], [B], and [C] assume the equilibrium values shown in Eqs. (2-18) through (2-20). Note that as G_0 increases, [A] decreases, [B] increases, and [C] may either increase or decrease depending on whether $(k_6 - k_3)$ is positive or negative.

The flux of material around the cycle is

$$\mathscr{F}_{AB} = \frac{G_0(k_3 k_5 + k_3 k_6 + k_4 k_6)}{l(k_2 k_4 + k_2 k_5 + k_3 k_5 + k_1 k_4 + k_1 k_5 + k_4 k_6 + k_1 k_3 + k_2 k_6 + k_3 k_6)} \quad (2\text{-}40)$$

a quantity directly proportional to G_0. In principle, we can compute the L function by considering the isolation of the system in contact with a reservoir of temperature T' and concentrations [A(T')], [B(T')], and [C(T')]. The probability of a fluctuation to A, B, C can be derived from a free energy argument since at T', we can determine the Helmholtz free energy of each species as a function of concentration.

A series of experiments carried out by Groth and his co-workers (6) gives experimental evidence for the existence of cycles and shows how a relatively simple system exhibits behavior surprisingly like some features of the terrestrial ecosystem. They first investigated the primary photochemical dissociation of CO_2 and H_2O by light from a xenon lamp (mostly 1470 and 1295 Å) and established the following primary reactions:

$$CO_2 + h\nu \rightarrow CO + O$$
$$H_2O + h\nu \rightarrow OH + H \qquad (2\text{-}41)$$

When mixtures of H_2O and CO_2 were irradiated, aldehydes and free oxygen were formed for which they proposed the reactions:

$$H + CO \rightarrow HCO$$
$$2HCO \rightarrow H_2CO + CO \qquad (2\text{-}42)$$
$$O + O \rightarrow O_2$$

However, it is also known (7) that in the presence of ultraviolet radiation, "When mixed with oxygen, formaldehyde undergoes a chain reaction giving, among other products, carbon monoxide, carbon dioxide, and water." In any case, aldehydes and oxygen will spontaneously react to yield carbon dioxide and water. The overall reaction scheme can then be represented as:

$$CO_2 + H_2O \xrightleftharpoons{h\nu} \text{aldehydes and } O_2$$

This is, of course, a cycle in terms of our previous analysis. It is indeed a good physical representation of what is embodied in the cycling theorem. The reaction scheme presented is an obvious oversimplification since more complex reaction products will form after prolonged irradiation.

What is perhaps most fascinating is that in a very simple laboratory system, there emerge many of the significant features of biological photosynthesis and the ecological carbon cycle. That is, we have CO_2 photosynthetically fixed into a carbohydrate which is subsequently oxidized, yielding energy and returning the carbon to CO_2. Last, we note that this is an example of the energy flow principle; the flow of energy through the CO_2–H_2O system is leading to a degree of chemical organization, indicated qualitatively by the existence of more complex molecular species such as the aldehydes.

The existence of cycles does not depend on the form of the energy flux, although the chemical details of the system will certainly be a function of the atomic composition and the nature of the sources ·and sinks. Therefore, it is of interest to examine the carbon dioxide–water system when it is subjected to an entirely different type of energy input. In the experiment of Garrison et al. (8), an aqueous solution of carbon dioxide was irradiated with a beam of 40 MeV alpha particles from a cyclotron.

Using C^{14} as a label in the original CO_2, radiation-induced products were analyzed. For a pure CO_2–H_2O system there was an appreciable yield of formic acid, HCOOH. In the presence of ferrous sulfate there was a demonstrable production of formaldehyde. Although no measurement was made, it is clear that some molecular oxygen must have been produced in this experiment.

The similarities between this α-particle radiation experiment and Groth's photochemical experiments are clear. Raising the energy of the system produces certain preferred reaction products. The detailed nature and distribution of these products is a problem in chemical kinetics for each specific case.

An alternate method for the study of cycling is to employ irreversible thermodynamics. Consider a case in which there is a flow of heat, a flow of matter, and chemical reactions. We may then write the following equation for the local entropy production (9):

$$\frac{\partial s_v}{\partial t} = -\text{div}\left(\frac{\mathbf{J}_q - \sum_{i=1}^{n} \mu_i \mathbf{J}_i}{T}\right) + \mathbf{J}_q \cdot \text{grad}\left(\frac{1}{T}\right)$$

$$+ \sum_{i=1}^{n} \mathbf{J}_i \cdot \text{grad}\left(\frac{-\mu_i}{T}\right) - \sum \frac{\mu_i v_i}{T} \tag{2-43}$$

where

$\mathbf{J}_q$ is the heat flow vector,
$\mathbf{J}_i$ is the flow vector of the ith species,
μ_i is the chemical potential of the ith species,
v_i is the local reaction velocity summed over all reactions involving the ith species,

$\mathbf{J}_q - \sum_{i=1}^{n} \mu_i \mathbf{J}_i$ is the total energy flow vector.

In the steady state,

$$\text{div}\left(\mathbf{J}_q - \sum_{i=1}^{n} \mu_i \mathbf{J}_i\right) = 0 \tag{2-44}$$

$$-\text{div } \mathbf{J}_i + v_i = \frac{\partial C_i}{\partial t} = 0 \tag{2-45}$$

Equations (2-43), (2-44), and (2-45) lead to the following steady state expression for local entropy production,

$$\frac{\partial s_v}{\partial t} = -\sum_i \frac{\text{div } \mathbf{J}_i \mu_i}{T} \tag{2-46}$$

In the steady state, the parameters become constant with time and the total entropy of the intermediate system becomes constant,

$$\int \frac{\partial s_v}{\partial t} \, dV = -\int \frac{\sum \text{div } \mathbf{J}_i \mu_i}{T} \, dV = 0 \tag{2-47}$$

T is always positive, hence div $\sum \mathbf{J}_i \mu_i$ must sometimes be positive and sometimes negative. The vector $\sum \mathbf{J}_i \mu_i$ is the flow of chemical energy. Equation (2-47) indicates that chemical energy flows around the system from internal sources to sinks. This flow must be accompanied by the flow of matter. Since the matter does not accumulate in the steady state, it must cycle around the system to accommodate the energy flows indicated in this equation.

The case just treated is a more generalized view of the type of problem previously treated with the Knudsen barrier and an isomerization reaction. The present treatment is restricted, by the usual limitations of irreversible thermodynamics, to situations near enough to equilibrium for local entropy to be a meaningful measure. It does, however, indicate that the simultaneous existence of temperature gradients and chemical reactions leads to cyclic flows of material within the system.

Finally, we shall conclude this chapter with a qualitative indication that in the types of systems we are discussing, the measure of the order of the system, the L function, has at least one maximum as a function of energy flow through the system, G_0. To do this we will adopt the approach of Eq. (1-26) and we will define the order function as

$$L = \frac{A_s - A_{eq}}{kT} \tag{2-48}$$

This corresponds to an isothermal constant volume isolation and is appropriate to a canonical ensemble; T is the kinetic temperature of the nonequilibrium system as previously defined; A_{eq} is the Helmholtz free energy for the equilibrium case and is completely defined; A_s is a steady state Helmholtz free energy and must be defined since it does not follow directly from thermodynamics. However, the steady state must correspond to a certain probability distribution of states which occurs in the equilibrium distribution. Designate the probability of these states as p_j. Then we can write

$$U_s = \sum p_j \epsilon_j \tag{2-49}$$

$$A_s = U_s - TS_s \tag{2-50}$$

$$L = \frac{U_s - U_{eq}}{kT} + \frac{S_{eq} - S_s}{k} \tag{2-51}$$

$$S_s = -k \sum_j p_j \ln p_j \tag{2-52}$$

The p_j terms are a normalized set of probabilities which define the non-equilibrium state; they need not relate to the p_j for the canonical ensemble. For G_0 equal to zero, L is equal to zero. For very small energy flow the state may be regarded as a fluctuation about equilibrium and linear theory can be used. S_{eq} is a maximum, hence, the second term is positive. U_s must involve a higher population of upper-lying energy levels compared to the equilibrium state so that the first term is also positive. Hence, dL/dG_0 is positive in the region of $G_0 = 0$.

As energy is added to the system a redistribution of states occurs. We will consider this energy in two parts, thermal energy and electronic energy. Thermal energy equipartitions and therefore includes the usual translational, rotational, and vibrational degrees of freedom. As G_0 increases, the population of electronic states above the ground state goes up; that is, there begins to form appreciable quantities of compounds other than those existing in the ground state. This is a necessary feature for chemical organization. As the energy flow increases, higher and higher energy levels become accessible and more and more chemical possibilities become available to the system. However, this cannot proceed indefinitely because it is limited by certain physical properties characteristic of all molecules. If the total amount of electronic energy of a molecule becomes too high the molecule dissociates, forming free radicals and ions. Thus, having passed through a state of high chemical organization, the system proceeds to states which are more and more chaotic at the molecular level. All reaction rates become extremely high, no stable compounds can be maintained, and the chemical system passes into a dense plasma.† Except at an extremely low pressure, a plasma cannot be maintained at a low temperature, therefore, the very high energy states of our system must be accompanied by high temperatures.

† A plasma is defined by Thompson (10) as follows: "When a gas is raised to a sufficiently high temperature, the atoms and molecules of the gas may become ionized, electrons being stripped off by the violent collisions consequent on the thermal agitation of the particles. When this happens, the dynamical behaviour of the gas may be dominated by the electromagnetic forces acting on the free ions and electrons, and its properties become sufficiently different from those of a normal unionized gas to merit the introduction of a new name, the 'plasma,' to denote a gas in such a highly ionized state."

Thus, biological organization as we know it, depending on relatively stable molecules, can only exist in a certain range of energy flux. We shall discuss this further when we make contact with the ecological consequences of solar energy flux.

To show that L has at least one maximum, we must demonstrate that there is a value G_0 for which dL/dG_0 is negative. We proceed to split U into its electronic and thermal parts

$$U = U_{el} + \eta kT \tag{2-53}$$

where η is a measure of the number of particles in the system. Then we can write

$$\frac{\Delta L}{\Delta G_0} =$$

$$\frac{1}{\Delta G_0}\left\{\left[\frac{U_s(G_0 + \Delta G_0) - U_{eq}(G_0 + \Delta G_0)}{k(T + \Delta T)} + \frac{S_{eq}(G_0 + \Delta G_0) - S_s(G_0 + \Delta G_0)}{k}\right]\right.$$

$$\left. -\left[\frac{U_s(G_0) - U_{eq}(G_0)}{kT} + \frac{S_{eq}(G_0) - S_s(G_0)}{k}\right]\right\} \tag{2-54}$$

The thermal energy term drops out and we have

$$\frac{\Delta L}{\Delta G_0} = \frac{\Delta U_{el}(G_0 + \Delta G_0)}{k(T + \Delta T)} - \frac{\Delta U_{el}(G_0)}{kT}$$

$$-\frac{\Delta S(G_0 + \Delta G_0)}{k} + \frac{\Delta S(G_0)}{k} \tag{2-55}$$

For a highly ionized plasma, we have almost reached a maximum of U_{el} so that U_{el} and, consequently, ΔU_{el} can increase only very slowly with G_0. The denominator, however, increases linearly with G_0 (condition of steady state). Hence, the sum of the first two terms is negative.

As all reactions occur with extreme rapidity, the major difference between the steady state and the isolated state are those molecules, radicals, or ions that are at higher energy states than in the equilibrium state. Since they have such short half-lives, they form a very small fraction of the total particles, and the probability distributions of the equilibrium and excited states approach each other. Thus, each ΔS approaches zero, the difference approaches zero, and $\Delta L/\Delta G_0$ is negative.

At very low flows the system approaches equilibrium with the thermal sink; at very high flows the system approaches equilibrium with what must effectively be a very hot source. Order generally means that the system has a character different than equilibrium systems. At both extremes of flow, this condition fails to obtain. Sustained order must therefore be a property of systems of intermediate flow rate. We will return to a discussion of this point in Chapter VI.

References

1. I. Prigogine, "Introduction to the Thermodynamics of Irreversible Processes." C. C. Thomas, Springfield, Illinois, 1955.
2. T. Hill, "An Introduction to Statistical Thermodynamics." Addison-Wesley, Reading, Massachusetts, 1960.
3. L. Onsager, *Phys. Rev.* **37**, 405 (1931).
4. L. Onsager, *Phys. Rev.* **38**, 2265 (1931).
5. H. J. Morowitz, *J. Theoret. Biol.* **13**, 60 (1966).
6. W. Groth, *in* "Photochemistry in the Liquid and Solid States" (F. Daniels, ed.), p. 21. Wiley, New York, 1960.
7. W. A. Noyes and P. A. Leighton, "The Photochemistry of Gases." Reinhold, New York, 1941.
8. W. M. Garrison, D. C. Morrison, J. G. Hamilton, A. A. Benson, and M. Calvin, *Science* **114**, 416 (1951).
9. A. Katchalsky and P. R. Curran, "Nonequilibrium Thermodynamics in Biophysics." Harvard Univ. Press, Cambridge, Massachusetts, 1965.
10. W. B. Thompson, "An Introduction to Plasma Physics." Addison-Wesley, Reading, Massachusetts, 1962.

III

Biological Generalizations and Equilibrium Organic Chemistry

Ought we, for instance, to begin by discussing each separate species—man, lion, ox, and the like—taking each kind in hand independently of the rest, or ought we rather to deal first with the attributes which they have in common in virtue of some common element of their nature, and proceed from this as a basis for the consideration of them separately?

Aristotle, in "De Partibus Animalium"

In the previous two chapters we have concentrated attention on the most general aspects of molecular organization as a problem in thermal physics, using such idealizations as perfect gases and local entropy. This feature of the problem has proven instructive since we have been able to show that the tendency to organize is a very general property of a certain class of physical systems and is not specifically dependent on living processes. Molecular organization and material cycles need not be viewed as uniquely biological characteristics; they are general features of all energy flow systems. Rather than being properties of biological systems, they are properties of the environmental matrix in which biological systems can arise and flourish.

In extraterrestrial exploration we therefore can and should look for living systems within the context of the general molecular organization imposed by the energy flux through the planetary surface. We need not restrict ourselves to carbon chemistry in searching for organizational features that may be biological or prebiological in nature. We may indeed follow Bernal's generalized definition of biology (1), "A true biology in its full sense would be the study of the nature and activity of all organized objects wherever they were to be found—on this planet, on others in the solar system, in other solar systems, in other galaxies—and at all times, future and past."

However, in addition to the general theory previously discussed we are also interested in specific types of organization which can come about in a terrestrial-type system made up of the familiar atoms of organic chemistry and biological chemistry. We must therefore extend our inquiry and, of necessity, introduce more chemical detail into our analysis. It is also necessary to consider the nature of the actual energy sources and sinks which are currently operative and which have been operative during the periods of biological and prebiological evolution.

In order to examine the biosphere in a theoretical context, we must consider a number of empirical generalizations which have emerged from the study of biochemistry, ultrastructure, genetics, bioenergetics, and ecology. Within the framework of these generalizations we will be able to begin the detailed study of biological systems in terms of thermal physics. These generalizations range from almost tautologous truisms to tentative hypotheses which require further study and confirmation. The progress of theoretical biology depends on our success in formulating biological laws which may then be reduced to physical foundations or, in their own right, be accorded the status of primitive postulates.

At this point it seems proper to extend our apologia for theoretical

45

biology. Biology and biochemistry have historically been sciences deeply rooted in empiricism and tinged with suspicion of "arm chair" or theoretical efforts. The mass of available information has been so large that finding exceptions to generalizations has been child's play. Theory, as that word is recognized by the physicist and the chemist, has been able to play only a small role in the progress of biology. Nevertheless, it must be realized that empiricism has its limits, and we must face the fact that a deeper understanding of biology may require a more heuristic approach. The making of new theories is, however, a risky business and much stumbling can be anticipated along the way to successful, general, and fruitful results. It is to the advantage of the science of biology to encourage these efforts rather than to concentrate on the failures which must accompany any very difficult and worthwhile set of tasks.

We shall proceed with a brief discussion of each of the generalizations. Following this discussion we will outline some methods of theoretical analysis which may be applied starting from the empirical laws.

Generalization I.   The major component of all functioning biological systems is water.

The water content of functioning living forms varies from 50% to over 95%. The chemistry of living systems is carried out in aqueous solutions or at water interfaces. Water is an important metabolite as well as a solvent. Some alteration is possible in the solvent component of living systems. It has been shown (2) that *Escherichia coli* and *Bacillus subtilis* will grow in a concentration of glycerol of up to 35%. In these experiments the glycerol concentration of the cellular fluid was approximately equal to that of the medium. In addition, in a large number of biological systems it has been possible to replace most of the normal water by deuterium oxide. Nevertheless, water is the primary component and under normal conditions the interior environments of cells is aqueous. In thermodynamic calculations on living systems it is therefore necessary to include information on heats and entropies of solution as well as heats and entropies of dilution. Much of these data are, unhappily, not available.

Generalization II.   The major atomic components in the covalently bonded portions of all functioning biological systems are carbon, hydrogen, nitrogen, oxygen, phosphorus, and sulfur.

This group of relatively low atomic weight elements has been given the mnemonic CHNOPS by Armstrong *et al.* (*3*). These elements are involved in the overwhelming amount of covalent bonding taking place in living organisms and must form the basis of our studies on bond distribution and electronic energy levels in biological materials. The experimental evidence for this generalization comes from biogeochemical data on the elemental composition of whole organisms and whole systems, as well as a general consideration of those compounds which play a significant role in biochemistry. The biochemical data will be considered in generalization III.

TABLE 3-1

RANGE OF VALUES OF THE PERCENTAGE OF BODY WEIGHT OF THE PRINCIPAL
ATOMIC COMPONENTS OF LIVING SYSTEMS[a]

Primary, 1–60%	Secondary, 0.05–1%	Microconstituents, 0.05% or less
C	Na	B
H	Mg	Fe
N	S	Si
O	Cl	Mn
P	K	Cu
	Ca	I
		Co
		Mo
		Zn

[a] Webb and Fearon (*4*).

Data from the early studies of Webb and Fearon (*4*) established the categories of atoms in living systems shown in Table 3-1. More detailed data on the atomic compositions of a number of specific organisms are given in Table 3-2. Consideration of these data leaves little doubt that biochemistry is primarily the chemistry of carbon, hydrogen, nitrogen, oxygen, phosphorus, and sulfur. In considering these data, it is worth bearing in mind that while in equilibrium chemical thermodynamics the major components dominate, in kinetic analysis minor components may have a disproportionately large effect on the state of the system.

TABLE 3-2

ATOMIC COMPOSITION OF FOUR REPRESENTATIVE SPECIES OF ORGANISMS[a]

Element	Man (5)	Alfalfa (5)	Copepod (6) (*Calanus finmarchicus*)	Bacteria (7, 8)
C	19.37	11.34	6.10	12.14
H	9.31	8.72	10.21	9.94
N	5.14	0.825	1.52	3.04
O	62.81	77.90	79.99	73.68
P	0.63	0.71	0.13	0.60
S	0.64	0.10	0.14	0.32
CHNOPS total:	97.90	99.60	98.09	99.72
Ca	1.38	0.58	0.04	0.03
Na	0.26	0.03	0.54	0.06
K	0.22	0.17	0.29	0.05
Mg	0.04	0.08	0.03	0.03
Cl	0.18	0.07	1.05	—
Major ion total:	2.08	0.93	1.95	0.17
Fe	0.0050	0.0027	0.0070	—
Si	0.0040	0.0093	0.0070	—
Zn	0.0025	0.0004	0.0000	—
Rb	0.0009	0.0005	0.0000	—
Cu	0.0004	0.0003	0.0000	—
Br	0.0002	0.0001	0.0009	—
Sn	0.0002	0.0000	0.0000	—
Mn	0.0001	0.0004	0.0000	—
I	0.0001	0.0000	0.0002	—
Al	0.0001	0.0025	0.0000	—
Pb	0.0001	0.0000	0.0000	—

[a] This table presents detailed data on the atomic composition of two animal species, one plant species, and one microbial species. The bacterial data were not directly given in the references cited but were calculated from information given plus a few assumptions. The copepods are a class of minute aquatic crustacea. The low nitrogen content of alfalfa reflects the fact that plants are primarily carbohydrate and contain relatively little protein.

Generalization III. Most of the dry mass of functioning biological systems consists of proteins, lipids, carbohydrates, and nucleic acids.

This generalization is part of the extremely ubiquitous scheme of biochemistry. The regularities go beyond the existence of common macromolecules, pathways, and intermediates. For example, most enzymes have a very similar amino acid composition, ribosomal RNA has a similar composition in all cells, and genetic coding is apparently universal. Other regularities occur in fatty acids and polysaccharides. The detailed distribution of the components listed in generalization III is also an ecological variable. The lowest trophic level is heavily carbohydrate, whereas at higher trophic levels proteins and lipids predominate. This variation is related to energy flow in ecology and will be discussed in Chapter V. In Table 3-3 we list the composition of some species for which data are available. This list is predominantly for animal species because, as already noted, plants abound in carbohydrates. In any case,

TABLE 3-3

MACROMOLECULAR COMPOSITION OF ORGANISMS
EXPRESSED AS PERCENT DRY WEIGHT

Organism	Protein	Lipid	Carbohydrate	Nucleic acid	Total of measured components	Ref.
Chlorella (unfavorable environment)	13.1	63.4	23.5		100.0	(*10*)
Eel (silver)	33.6	63.8	—		97.4	(*12*)
Sacchromyces cerevisiae	40	2	37	12	91.0	(*11*)
Herring	45.7	49.5	—		95.2	(*12*)
Chlorella (favorable environment)	46.4	20.2	33.4		100.0	(*10*)
Oyster	51.2	11.1	28.2		89.5	(*9*)
Torulopsis utilis	54.4	3	30	4.6	92	(*11*)
Silkworm (larva)	55.5	13.3	1.8		70.6	(*9*)
Eel (yellow)	58.0	39.4	—		97.4	(*12*)
Sea urchin (40 hours larva)	60.6	17.4	3.4		81.4	(*9*)
Silkworm (imago)	63.4	24.3	6.5		94.2	(*9*)
Sea urchin (unfertilized egg)	66.9	31.2	5.4		103.5	(*9*)
Mussel	73.7	11.9	—		85.6	(*12*)
Plaice	79.5	9.4	—		88.9	(*12*)
Mycoplasma gallisepticum	80	11	—	12	103	(*13*)

there are only four major classes of macromolecules which make up the overwhelming fraction of structural material in living cells.

Generalization IV. There is a ubiquitous and restricted set of small organic molecules which constitutes a very large fraction of the total mass of all cellular systems.

This generalization is again a statement of the uniformity of biochemistry. It is one of the very significant, if infrequently discussed, results of that science. Amidst the enormous diversity of biological types, including millions of recognizable species, the number of biochemical pathways is small, restricted, and ubiquitously distributed. All protein is made from the same group of amino acids, all RNA from the same group of ribonucleotides, all DNA from the same group of deoxyribonucleotides, all carbohydrates from a restricted group of sugars, and all phospholipids from a relatively small group of fatty acids. Thus, in most cases, over 90% of the cellular material can be accounted for in less than 50 compounds and polymers of these compounds.

If one considers the group of low molecular weight compounds (less than 500 daltons) which can be made from carbon, hydrogen, nitrogen, oxygen, phosphorus, and sulfur, this number is in the billions or higher. Yet out of this potential group, a very small subgroup is actually used. An instructive estimate of the size of this subgroup can be obtained from "The Pfizer Handbook of Microbial Metabolites" (*14*). This book is a compilation of data on the structural and simpler physical properties of all the primary microorganisms metabolites which have been reported to be produced by the organisms growing either in the wild state or in culture on artificial sugar-based medium.

The surprising thing is that this list contains only 1313 compounds. Many of these compounds are confined to very few species, as is the case with penicillin. The list of ubiquitous compounds which should include all the absolutely essential ones is a much smaller list and may only encompass a few hundred substances. The generalization may either be a historical one stemming from a common origin, or may be derivable from a more fundamental principle. Certain perplexing questions about the occurrence of these small molecules suggest the usefulness of searching for a fundamental principle. For instance, alanine and valine are ubiquitous constituents of protein, while α-aminobutyric acid, which is widely distributed in biological systems,

TABLE 3.4—continued

Sugars and Derivatives

Glucose	2-Phosphoglyceric acid
Glucose-6-phosphate	Phosphopyruvic acid
Fructose-6-phosphate	Pyruvic acid
Fructose-1,6-diphosphate	Lactic acid
Glyceraldehyde-3-phosphate	5-Phosphoribosyl-1-pyrophosphate
Dihydroxyacetone phosphate	D-Ribose
1,3-Diphosphoglyceric acid	D-2-Deoxyribose
3-Phosphoglyceric acid	Ribose-5-phosphate

Lipids and Precursors

Glycerol	α-Glycerol phosphate
Fatty acids	Ethanolamine

Purines, Pyrimidines, and Derivatives

Uracil	
Cytosine	
Thymine	Nucleosides, nucleotides including monophosphates, diphosphates,
Adenine	and triphosphates
Guanine	

Miscellaneous

Water	Phosphoric acid
Carbon dioxide	Succinic acid
Ammonia	Fumaric acid
Glutathione	Acetic acid
Carbamyl phosphate	

β-mercaptoethylamine as a component of coenzyme A is not included). The list is presented in Table 3-4.

These compounds and polymers of these compounds comprise the bulk of cellular biomass in most systems. They clearly reflect the atomic composition CHNOPS as has already been indicated. Such a list must of its very nature be tentative and open-ended. New findings may lead to organisms lacking one or more of these compounds and other compounds may prove to be of universal occurrence.

Generalization V. Biological information is structural.

A large number of biological systems have been held at temperatures near to absolute zero for varying periods of time. On rewarming, many of these systems continue their biological activity unimpaired (*19*). It appears to be a generalization of cryobiology that if a system survives the trauma of ice crystal formation, either on freezing or on thawing, then its function is unchanged by taking it to temperatures near to absolute zero. As an example of this type of low temperature experiment, consider a recent study done on *Artemia* (brine shrimp) eggs (*20*). The eggs were kept for six days at temperatures below $2°K$. Upon rewarming, their hatch rate was the same as control eggs held at room temperature.

At the molecular level, information can be stored in two ways, either in molecular structure, essentially in the specification of covalent or secondary bonds, or in dynamic processes such as the flow of intermediates or the conduction of electrical impulses. At absolute zero all processes cease and the system is pure structure. This structure retains all the relevant biological information.

The property being discussed here may be formulated in terms of classical statistical mechanics to gain some insight into the meaning of the generalization. We can classically describe a system in a multidimensional p, q space where the q's are coordinates and the p's are momenta (*21*). When we take the system to temperatures near absolute zero, we obliterate any information about the original configuration in p space and confine the system to a very tiny subvolume in this space. Raising the temperature involves a randomization in momentum space. Since the rewarmed system is biologically functional, the information must be stored in coordinates in q space.

This generalization may seem at odds with our previous assertion that energy flow is necessary to maintain order. Biological information is stored in molecules which are unstable for long periods at ordinary temperatures; they are constantly undergoing thermal degradation. Near absolute zero these processes cease and the information-storing structures are indefinitely stable. Thus, although information storage is structural, energy flow is normally required to restore structures as fast as they are being degraded.

The significance of this generalization becomes clear if we consider the *de novo* synthesis of a biological self-replicating system. It implies that making a living cell is a matter of synthesizing the right structure; it is a very complicated problem in organic chemistry. If we have the appropriate spatial array of atoms in the right environment, then the necessary living processes automatically follow.

Generalization VI. The flow of energy in the biosphere is accompanied by the formation and hydrolysis of phosphate bonds, usually those of adenosine triphosphate.

In muscle contraction, firefly luminescence, electric eel discharge, or the driving of chemical reactions, the energy at the last step appears to come universally from the hydrolysis of an "energy-rich phosphate bond." This generalization is related to generalization IV, regarding ubiquitous compounds. A restricted biochemistry leads to restricted methods of energy transfer and utilization. The almost universal occurrence of adenosine triphosphate appears to have further consequences in terms of control and metabolic stability. Almost all reaction pathways go through at least one stage involving reactions with ATP, ADP, and phosphate. Thus, the concentrations of these intermediates exert some degree of overall control of cell metabolic activity.

The experimental evidence for the ubiquity of phosphate reactions was put in general form by Lipmann in 1941 (22). A detailed reexamination of bioenergetics in terms of biochemistry was published by Krebs and Kornberg in 1957 (23). A modern and elementary exposition of the role of phosphate bonds in biological processes is given in the recent book by Lehninger (24). We will return to the ecological significance of ATP in Chapter V.

The role of phosphates as universal intermediates deserves considerable study in order to understand the fundamental energetic mechanisms in terms of the molecular physics of these compounds.

Generalization VII. Sustained life under present-day conditions is a property of an ecological system rather than a single organism or species.

A one-species ecological system is never found. The carbon cycle requires at least one primary producer and a method of returning carbon to the CO_2 pool. A system of only herbivores would die of starvation. A system of only primary producers would grind to a halt from CO_2 exhaustion unless autolysis produced CO_2 at a sufficient rate. This does not appear to occur. This generalization is an ecological example of cycles in steady state systems.

Traditional biology has tended to concentrate attention on individual organisms rather than the biological continuum. The origin of life is thus looked for as a unique event in which an organism arises from the surrounding milieu. A more ecologically balanced point of view would examine the ecological cycles and subsequent chemical systems which must have developed and flourished for a considerable period before anything resembling organisms appeared.

Generalization VIII. Functioning biological systems are cellular in nature.

This generalization is a restatement of the cell theory. For purposes of this discussion we do not require a strong statement of the theory, merely the recognition that the minimum functioning biological unit is membrane-bounded and distinct. We also note that replication involves the production of new membrane-bounded distinct elements. This statement is therefore very closely related to generalization IX, dealing with membranes. The cellular mode of organization provides a method of preventing the loss of intermediates by diffusion. It also provides a method of exerting control on the internal environment. Returning to generalization VII, we might note that the mode of cellular organization provides a method of partially and temporarily isolating a portion of the ecosystem.

Generalization IX. There is a universal type of membrane structure utilized in all biological systems.

The empirical basis for this generalization comes from three separate lines of evidence.

(*a*) *Electron Microscopy (25).* All cells appear to be surrounded by a unit membrane which is a triple-layered structure on the order of 75 Å in thickness. The nuclear membrane is a similar structure. In addition, organelles such as mitochondria, chloroplasts, and other inclusions appear to be principally structured from similar membrane material.

(*b*) *Dielectric Dispersion Measurements (26).* Numerous studies have been carried out on the frequency dependent electrical impedance of suspensions of cells or organelles. From these studies it is possible to compute the electrical capacitance per unit area of the envelope of the structure being studied. For the biological materials that have been examined, the values range between 0.5 to 1.5 $\mu F/cm^2$.

(*c*) *Chemical Composition.* The limited work carried out on the chemical composition of membranes indicates that they are all predominantly lipoprotein in nature.

The universal character of unit membranes appears to be a property of the way in which phospholipid molecules can aggregate into sheetlike structures. The free energy change due to apolar bonds and electrostatic interaction of charged groups places restrictions on the minimum layer thickness of aggregated phospholipids in an aqueous environment. It should be noted that the unit membrane is not the only bonding envelope of most cells. Rigid cell walls, secondary membranes, and capsules are common in biological systems. The unit membrane is, however, the only one that is universally present and appears to be an irreducible minimum bounding element.

Generalization X. All populations of replicating biological systems give rise to mutant phenotypes which reflect altered genotypes.

This is an empirical generalization which is a *sine qua non* for the process of evolution as well as the science of genetics. This generalization has already been reduced to physics by the work of Delbruck and Schrödinger (*27*). One needs only to assume that genetic information is stored in large stable molecules (this may have been an assumption in 1945 when Schrödinger wrote his monograph—it is by now part of the dogma of modern biology). All such molecules have a non-zero probability of undergoing rearrangement to another state at temperatures other than absolute zero. The feature not immediately available from physics is the frequency of mutation and this depends on the structure of the physical gene and its structural modifications during replication and readout of information.

Generalization XI. All replicating cells have a genome made of deoxyribonucleic acid which stores the genetic information of the cells which may be read out in sequences of ribonucleotides and translated into polypeptides.

This is a condensed statement of many of the results of modern biochemical genetics and is often referred to as the central dogma, or Crick's central dogma. First, the physical gene is a segment of double-stranded deoxyribonucleic acid (DNA). Cell reproduction must involve the production of a new DNA genome. Second, the general validity of nucleic acid to amino acid coding is embodied in this generalization.

The evidence seems overwhelmingly in favor of triplet coding. Third, is the idea that messenger ribonucleic acid (RNA) is the intermediate between DNA and proteins. Fourth, is the concept that genes act by the specification of proteins, usually enzymes, which carry out particular cellular functions.

Generalization XII. All growing cells have ribosomes which are the site of protein synthesis.

Ribosomes appear to be universal organelles in biological systems. There is some variation among different groups of organisms as to the detailed size of ribosomes and distribution among size classes, but all cells which are capable of synthesizing protein have ribonucleoprotein particles which are between 80 and 200 Å in diameter and are approximately half RNA and half protein. The properties of ribosomes have recently been extensively reviewed by Petermann (28), who makes the following statement which is essentially the equivalent of generalization XII, "Since no alternate mechanism for protein synthesis has been established, one must assume that ribosomes are of universal occurrence in microorganisms, higher plants, and animals."

Generalization XIII. The translation of information from nucleotide language takes place through specific activating enzymes and transfer RNA.

The mechanism of protein synthesis has been found to be similar in all systems that have been studied. A specific enzyme catalyzes the formation of a complex between a given amino acid and molecule of transfer RNA, specific for that amino acid. It is this complex that then enters into the template process of protein synthesis. Both the transfer RNA and the activating enzyme are probably encoded in the cell's genome.

This completes our list of generalizations and establishes the kinds of systems that are encompassed in our concept of terrestrial biology. In the following pages we examine the study of some physical systems related by various common parameters to the biological systems we have been discussing. The first and most obvious common parameter to begin our inquiry with is atomic composition.

The biochemical data given in generalizations I–IV, when taken in conjunction with our general concepts of biochemistry, provide sufficient background to formulate a presumptive range of atomic composition consistent with terrestrial life. The distributions are dominated by water, with the general result that water constitutes between 50 and 99 % of the mass of functioning organisms. The crucial roles of carbon and nitrogen in the organic chemistry of biological compounds is another obvious, if by now trivial, conclusion to be drawn from these data.

We may now proceed from a totally nonbiological point of view to inquire into the range of chemical species which are possible within the limits imposed by atomic composition and other thermodynamic constraints. This cannot be done in a very axiomatic way, as there is no general theory of organic chemistry. The type of theory envisioned would consist of a set of rules which would generate the field of possible compounds and predict the properties of these compounds. The possibility of such theoretical developments is not being denied, rather it is being asserted that such a theory does not currently exist. Therefore, our approach to general problems of chemistry must be much more empirical; we must rely on measured thermodynamic properties of known compounds and utilize inductive methods to establish the general features that are of interest to us. This approach will be apparent in much of the tabulated data appearing in this chapter and in Chapter IV.

From the viewpoint we have adopted, a consideration of states of the system under energy flux can begin with a consideration of the equilibrium system. We return to a concept we introduced in Chapter I and raise the following question. If we have a container of volume V containing N_1 atoms of species 1, N_2 atoms of species 2, etc., and we allow this system to age for a very long time in contact with an infinite reservoir, at temperature T, what will be the chemical composition of the contents of the container in terms of molecular species?

In principle, it is possible to answer this question for a restricted range of conditions. Assume the concentrations N_i/V are small enough so that the equilibrium state will be a homogeneous gas phase. Next, assume that we have a list of all the molecular species that can be formed from these atoms as well as the free energies of formation of all species relative to some standard states of the elements. We may then designate, by n_i, the number of molecules of each species. The problem then reduces itself to finding a set of n_i consistent with the N_i and which leads to a minimum free energy for the entire system.

A limited calculation of this type was carried out by Suess (29), who considered the atomic species C, H, and O, and the molecular species

CO_2, CO, CH_4, H_2, H_2O. The following equilibrium equations were written:

$$K_1 = \frac{[CO][H_2O]}{[CO_2][H_2]} \tag{3-1}$$

$$K_2 = \frac{[H_2]^4[CO_2]}{[CH_4][H_2O]^2} \tag{3-2}$$

$$\Sigma\, C = [CO_2] + [CO] + [CH_4] \tag{3-3}$$

$$\Sigma\, O = 2[CO_2] + [CO] + [H_2O] \tag{3-4}$$

$$\Sigma\, H = 2[H_2] + 2[H_2O] + 4[CH_4] \tag{3-5}$$

Computer methods were used to solve the five simultaneous equations. The main purpose of this work was to explore the conditions under which elementary carbon and organic compounds form in thermodynamic equilibrium. Extension of this method would require a knowledge of the equilibrium constants of all possible reactions, which is equivalent to knowing all the free energies of formation.

A more general method directly using free energy minimization has been undertaken by Dayhoff et al. (30). They start out with a mathematical protocol devised by White et al. (31) who use the following approach. For a perfect gas mixture the Gibbs free energy is given by

$$F = \Sigma\, n_i\mu_i = \sum_i n_i\left(RT\ln\frac{n_i}{\Sigma\, n_i} + RT\ln p + \mu_{0i}\right) \tag{3-6}$$

where n_i is the mole number and μ_i is the Gibbs chemical potential of the ith species; μ_{0i} is the standard state chemical potential and p is the total pressure.

The determination of the equilibrium composition is equivalent to finding the set of non-negative values n_i which minimizes this free energy equation and satisfies the obvious mass balance constraints,

$$\sum_i a_{ij}n_i = b_j \tag{3-7}$$

where i designates the molecular species, a_{ij} the number of atoms of the jth type per molecule of the ith species, and b_j the total number of atoms.

The approach of White et al. (31) can be applied to the problem we originally formulated by a shift from the Gibbs free energy to the Helmholtz free energy. The former applies to systems at constant pressure, whereas we have formulated the problem for constant volume systems. If we note that $A = F - PV$, we can formulate the Helmholtz free energy of the system as

$$A = \sum n_i \left(RT \ln \frac{n_i}{V} + RT \ln \frac{RT}{e} + \mu_{0i} \right) \qquad (3\text{-}8)$$

Again, the solution of the equilibrium problem consists of minimizing A, subject to the conservation of mass constraints given earlier.

Dayhoff and co-workers have written a computer program utilizing the approach of White et al., adopted to an IBM 7090. The solution is approached by an iterative process. At each step, $M + 1$ linear equations are solved where M is the number of elements in the system. Twenty-five elements and over 500 compounds can be handled by the program. In the calculations the standard free energies of formation were obtained from National Bureau of Standards Tables or computed by summing the free energies of the component groups by the method of Van Kevelen and Chermin (32).

In Table 3-5 we present values of concentrations of molecular species obtained by Dayhoff et al. for the gas-phase thermodynamic equilibrium for a system having an atomic composition $C_2H_{10}NO_8$ and a temperature of 500°C. Inspection of this table indicates, as we have previously discussed, how unfavorable equilibrium conditions are for the formation of any quantity of biologically interesting molecules. In the lowest-lying energy states, the collection of molecules is dominated by water, carbon dioxide, nitrogen, and methane. To create an Oparin ocean [a solution of organic molecules postulated by A. I. Oparin (33) as a precursor to living systems], it is necessary to pump energy into the system in order to increase the concentration of molecules, which are energy-rich compared to the ground state distribution. Energy flow serves just this purpose, especially if it enters the system in some form of particularly high potential. The entry of energy into the system, whether it be by ultraviolet or visible radiation, ionizing radiation, spark discharge, or some other form, causes chemical reactions. These reactions produce a distribution of molecules energetically above the ground state. These molecules eventually react to go back toward the ground state. This sequence of events produces an entirely different distribution of compounds than observed in Table 3-5. If the inflow of energy is by photons, we may regard the process as a type of optical pumping which stores energy in the intermediate system. At the biological level photosynthetic processes act to optically pump CO_2 and H_2O into a state of carbohydrates and oxygen. All subsequent biological processes are driven by

TABLE 3-5

EQUILIBRIUM DISTRIBUTION OF COMPOUNDS FOR THE SYSTEM $C_2H_{10}NO_8$ AT 1 atm AND 500°C[a]

Compound	Equilibrium concentration	Compound	Equilibrium concentration
Water	2.24	Glycine	0.48×10^{-21}
Carbon dioxide	0.88	Acetylene	0.11×10^{-22}
Nitrogen	0.50	Lactic acid	0.20×10^{-23}
Methane	0.12	Acetamide	0.11×10^{-23}
Hydrogen	0.18×10^{-1}	Ethylene glycol	0.62×10^{-24}
Ammonia	0.15×10^{-3}	Benzene	0.52×10^{-25}
Carbon monoxide	0.54×10^{-4}	Alanine	0.97×10^{-27}
Ethane	0.34×10^{-7}	Furan	0.14×10^{-28}
Formic acid	0.93×10^{-9}	Pyrrole	0.31×10^{-30}
Acetic acid	0.25×10^{-9}	Pyridine	0.16×10^{-30}
Methanol	0.73×10^{-11}	Cyanogen	0.77×10^{-31}
Formaldehyde	0.13×10^{-11}	Benzoic acid	0.65×10^{-31}
Ethylene	0.88×10^{-13}	Pyruvic acid	0.31×10^{-31}
Hydrogen cyanide	0.73×10^{-13}	Pyrimidine	0.13×10^{-31}
Methylamine	0.64×10^{-13}	Phenol	0.10×10^{-31}
Acetaldehyde	0.81×10^{-14}	Xylene	0.17×10^{-33}
Ethanol	0.49×10^{-15}	Benzaldehyde	0.12×10^{-35}
Acetone	0.92×10^{-17}	Naphthalene	$< 10^{-38}$
Ketene	0.19×10^{-17}	Anthracene	$< 10^{-38}$
Methyl ether	0.30×10^{-19}	Asphalt	$< 10^{-38}$
Formamide	0.24×10^{-20}	Oxygen	$< 10^{-38}$

[a] This table has been adapted from Table I, p. 1463 of Dayhoff et al., Thermodynamic equilibria in prebiological atmospheres, Science 146, 1461 (1964). The concentrations shown have been recalculated by Dayhoff (personal communication) using the more recent free energy values shown in Dayhoff et al. Thermodynamic equilibrium in prebiological atmospheres of C, H, O, N, P, S, and Cl. NASA SP-3040 (1967). This has led to a change by a small factor in calculated equilibrium concentrations for some compounds; however, the conclusions are not affected.

reactions leading to the oxidation of the compounds back toward the equilibrium distribution of carbon dioxide and water. The type of calculation carried out by Dayhoff *et al.* could be extended to more complex situations by introducing additional steps into the program. Such an approach depends on the availability of reliable thermochemical data for all possible compounds, as well as an exhaustive catalog of such compounds. A group at the National Bureau of Standards, under the direction of George Armstrong, have undertaken a thorough literature search and analysis of existing thermochemical data of biological interest, and have published a number of reports making these data available on compounds of carbon, hydrogen, nitrogen, oxygen, sulfur, and phosphorus (*3, 34-40*). A serious difficulty in the molecular approach lies in the enormous number of possible compounds that must be dealt with. To make this point, as well as to establish a suitable beginning for generalized studies of this nature, we list in Appendix III all the compounds reported in the literature which are composed of the elements C, H, N, O, P, S and which contain either no carbon atoms or one carbon atom per molecule. The number of possible two-carbon compounds is considerably greater than one-carbon compounds. The number of potential compounds rises rapidly as a function of the carbon number. This question is examined in Appendix IV. In spite of these large numbers, some factors should be noted. The number of compounds containing n carbon atoms is finite and denumerable. Therefore, in principle, we can carry out a minimization calculation and predict equilibrium distributions. In general, only compounds with rather large negative free energies of formation per atom will form an appreciable part of the equilibrium distributions. Our ability to carry out this kind of program then depends on computer capacity, availability of thermodynamic data, and our patience in dealing with very large and complex systems.

If we wish to depart from gas-phase calculations, a number of new parameters now enters into consideration. The free energy of each species can no longer be written as an independent term, but complicated cross-terms must be introduced. One case that seems both accessible and of biological interest is that of very dilute aqueous solutions. This is a system of largely H and O with traces of C, N, P, and S. The free energies must now include heats and entropies of solution at high dilution, as well as the other terms in the gas-phase calculation. Considerably more thermodynamic data are required but, in principle, a minimization is possible.

An alternative approach can be taken to equilibrium calculations by concentrating on the distribution of bond types rather than the distribution of molecular species. This gives a much less complete characterization of the system, but allows more general treatments of certain features. This approach starts with two assumptions.

(1) In determining the equilibrium state, the internal energy term dominates the entropy term in the Helmholtz free energy $A = U - TS$. Actually, the condition is not quite so stringent, for we can concentrate on ΔA in the regions of interest and require that ΔU be large compared with $\Delta(TS)$. Phelps (41) has carried out some preliminary calculations of configurational entropies based on the number of permutations of atoms and bonds consistent with a given energy. This was a computer project restricted to the CHNO system. The numerical results do, however, support the notion that the ΔU term dominates the changes in Helmholtz free energy.

(2) U can be determined by assigning a unique heat of formation or heat of dissociation to each bond type. This is an approximation which, on the average, will probably be good to about 10 %. Under this approximation, $U = \sum E_i n_i$, where n_i is the number of bonds of the ith type and E_i is the bond energy. The discussion of the use of bond energies, as well as the best experimental values, will be found in the books of Vedeneyev et al. (42), Cottrell (43), and Pauling (44). The work by Cottrell is particularly useful in this connection.

For the CHNOPS system, the bonds of interest and the average bond energies are given in Table 3-6. These values are taken from Cottrell (43), except for four values which are taken from Huggins (45). More bond types may be allowed to generate a more complete system. For instance, Table 3-6 does not generate graphite or carbon monoxide among the possible molecular species, nor are benzene rings included.

The equilibrium state can be found by seeking a minimum to

$$A \cong \sum n_i E_i \qquad (3\text{-}9)$$

subject to the conservation of atoms constraints given in Eq. (3-7). This is a problem in linear programming for which computer methods are available.

Phelps (41) has carried out a minimization of this type on a CHNO system and has obtained the following results for a system consisting of 5.83×10^9 carbon atoms, 9.38×10^9 hydrogen atoms, 2.67×10^9 oxygen atoms, and 1.55×10^9 nitrogen atoms. The energy minimization in this

TABLE 3-6

AVERAGE BOND ENERGIES FOR COVALENT BONDS OF IMPORTANCE
IN COMPOUNDS OF THE CHNOPS SYSTEM[a]

Bond type	Bond energy (kcal/mole)	Bond type	Bond energy (kcal/mole)	Bond type	Bond energy (kcal/mole)
C—C	82.6	H—H	104.2	O—O	41
C=C	145.8	H—N	93.4	O=O	119.1
C≡C	199.6	H—O	110.6	O—P[b]	84
C—H	98.7	H—P	77	O=P	120
C—N	72.8	H—S	83.0	O—S	
C=N	147	N—N	21	O=S	112
C≡N	212.6	N=N[c]	100	P—P	48
C—O	85.5	N≡N	225.8	P=P	
C=O	174	N—O	53	P≡P	116.7
C—P[b]	62	N=O	145	P—S[b]	55
C=P		N—P[b]	50	P=S	
C≡P		N=P		S—S	54
C—S	65	N≡P	138	S=S	84

[a] From Cottrell (43).   [b] From Huggins (45).   [c] From Pauling (44).

calculation occurs for the following bond distribution: 4.04×10^9 carbon hydrogen single bonds (C—H), 9.64×10^9 carbon carbon single bonds (C—C), 0.78×10^9 nitrogen nitrogen triple bonds (N≡N), and 5.34×10^9 oxygen hydrogen single bonds (O—H).

The atomic composition values chosen corresponded to estimates of the atomic composition of the nonaqueous portion of the bacterium *Escherichia coli* (46). This cell contains about 2×10^{10} atoms in the nonaqueous portion. The computed energy minimum was 7.482×10^{10} eV.

We may examine the actual distributions of bonds in biological systems from the gross chemical composition in terms of amino acids, nucleotides, sugars, fatty acids, etc. Such an analysis has been carried out for *Escherichia coli* (46, 47), based primarily on the data of Roberts and co-workers (7); the results are presented in Table 3-7.

In carrying out these calculations of bond energies, the reference state is a collection of free atoms. The calculated bond energies are therefore negative quantities and the greater the value, the lower the energy state of the system. The lowest-lying state is therefore $(7.482 \times 10^{10} - 6.936 \times 10^{10})$ eV lower in bond energy than the living state. This difference of 0.546×10^{10} eV is the amount of energy enrichment necessary

TABLE 3-7

COVALENT BOND DISTRIBUTION IN *Escherichia coli*

Bond type	Bond energy (eV)	Numbers of bonds	Contribution to total bond energy (eV)
H—C	3.92	730×10^7	2862×10^7
H—N	3.65	160×10^7	584×10^7
H—O	4.79	48×10^7	230×10^7
C—C	2.87	393×10^7	1128×10^7
C=C	4.89	30×10^7	147×10^7
C—N	2.40	276×10^7	662×10^7
C=N	4.85	24×10^7	116×10^7
C—O	3.34	113×10^7	377×10^7
C=O	6.98	119×10^7	830×10^7
			$\overline{6.936 \times 10^{10}}$

to take a system from its lowest-lying state to one that is isoenergetic with living material.

These considerations allow us to attempt the calculation of $p_{L\,max}$, the maximum probability of a living cell arising in an equilibrium ensemble. This subject was introduced in Chapter I and Eq. (1-5) represents the formalism to be used in the numerical calculation. We can rewrite this equation in the following way.

$$p_{L\,max} = \frac{\int_{\epsilon_m}^{\infty} \omega(\epsilon)e^{-\epsilon/kT}\,d\epsilon}{\int_{\epsilon_1}^{\infty} \omega(\epsilon)e^{-\epsilon/kT}\,d\epsilon} \tag{3-10}$$

where $\omega(\epsilon)$ is the degeneracy associated with the energy value ϵ. The previously discussed studies (41) indicate that $\omega(\epsilon)$ is a slowly varying function of ϵ when compared to $e^{-\epsilon/kT}$. We can therefore get an approximate solution by considering $\omega(\epsilon)$ a constant and moving it out in front of the integral sign. We then get

$$p_{L\,max} = \exp{-\frac{(\epsilon_m - \epsilon_1)}{kT}}$$

$$\cong 10^{-10^{11}} \tag{3-11}$$

The difference between the bond energies of the biosphere and the minimum energy state of the system is an important conceptual parameter because it indicates the energy enrichment of the biosphere due to energy flow processes. While the preliminary numerical values should not be taken too seriously, they establish orders of magnitude which are useful in assessing the actual energy flow situation. The calculated energy difference of 0.546×10^{10} eV is distributed among 2×10^{10} atoms or 0.27 eV per atom represents the energy stored in the biosphere. Actually this number is too high since it includes only the nonaqueous portion of the biosphere. Including water, this number becomes approximately 0.07 eV per atom, or about 1.5 kcal/mole of atoms.

The quantity $(\epsilon_m - \epsilon_1)/kT$ is an extensive property of the system. For that reason, the size of the postulated living cells plays a major role in the calculation of $p_{L\,max}$, the probability of a living system arising in an equilibrium ensemble. An unfavorably small value would be obtained by choosing too large a cell. If we consider one of the smallest reported bacteria, *Dialister pneumosintes*, the data of Cheng (*48*) indicate a dry

TABLE 3-8

PROBABILITY OF A SYSTEM OCCURRING AS A SPONTANEOUS FLUCTUATION
IN AN EQUILIBRIUM ENSEMBLE FOR SYSTEMS OF DIFFERENT SIZES

(The quantity $p_{L\,max} \times 10^{134}$ is the upper limit of the probability that such a fluctuation would have occurred in the history of the universe.)

System	$p_{L\,max}$	$p_{L\,max} \times 10^{134}$
Escherichia coli	$10^{-10^{11}}$	$10^{-10^{11}}$
Dialister pneumosintes	$10^{-10^{10}}$	$10^{-10^{10}}$
Mycoplasma hominis H39	$10^{-5 \times 10^9}$	$10^{-5 \times 10^9}$
T2 Phage	$10^{-2 \times 10^8}$	$10^{-2 \times 10^8}$
ϕX 174	$10^{-2 \times 10^6}$	$10^{-1,999,866}$
Hemoglobin molecule	$10^{-4 \times 10^4}$	$10^{-39,866}$
Ribonuclease molecule	10^{-8000}	10^{-7866}
Amino acid	10^{-60}	10^{+74}

structure of approximately 2×10^9 atoms, or one-tenth the mass of *E. coli*. The smallest living cells are *Mycoplasma*. One of the smallest of these, *Mycoplasma hominis* H39, has a genome of only about 500,000,000 daltons as reported by Bode and Morowitz (*49*). This corresponds to a nonaqueous portion of about 10^9 atoms. For both of these cells $p_{L\,max}$ is still vanishingly small. Table 3-8 gives values of $p_{L\,max}$ for a number of systems; the last column lists $p_{L\,max}$ multiplied by the quantity 10^{134}. The maximum instantaneous probability is multiplied by the total number of chances to obtain an upper limit to the probability that the event has happened once in the history of the universe. Note that the amino acid value of $p_{L\,max}$ of 10^{-60} is consistent with the very small amino acid values reported in Table 3-5. There we noted that the amount of glycine is 4×10^{-22} moles in a system made up of approximately 10 moles of atoms. To compare the probabilities in Tables 3-5 and 3-8, we normalize the data in Table 3-5 to a system containing just the requisite atoms to make one glycine molecule. This leads to a probability of a glycine being present at equilibrium of the order of 10^{-45}. This compares with the rough amino acid figure of 10^{-60} in Table 3-8. Considering the nature of these types of calculations, these values can be considered to be in line. What is very clear, however, from an examination of either Table 3-5 or Table 3-8, is that if equilibrium processes alone were at work, the largest possible fluctuation in the history of the universe is likely to have been no larger than a small peptide. Again, we stress in a very firm quantitative way, the impossibility of considering life originating as a fluctuation in an equilibrium ensemble.

In summary then, for a system of any appreciable number of atoms (larger than 30), there is a vanishingly small probability of an energy fluctuation being large enough to take an equilibrium system up to the potential level required of biomass. On the other hand, an energy enrichment of 0.07 eV/atom, the average amount required for biomass, is easily achieved in an energy flux situation. This problem may be formulated in the following way. Suppose that we designate $\bar{\epsilon}$ the mean energy per atom of the biosphere above that of the lowest energy state. Then if $\bar{t}$ is the mean time that energy spends in the system between source and sink, the necessary flow rate per atom is

$$f = \frac{\bar{\epsilon}}{\bar{t}} \qquad (3\text{-}12)$$

Equation (3-12) does not have any meaning in a strict physical sense, since energy loses its identity when it enters the system and there is no way to label energy by tracers. However, an analogous equation exists for the flow of a species of atoms or molecules through any arbitrary system. This equation is of the form

Flow of species $\times$ mean residence time = Total amount of species
$$\text{in the system} \qquad (3\text{-}13)$$

This equation is very general and is used in such diverse fields as geochemistry, hemodynamics, and sanitary engineering. In the case under consideration, Eq. (3-13) confers meaning to Eq. (3-12), since the flow of energy into the biosphere is always accompanied by the flow of CO_2 into the system, and the mean residence time for energy can be taken as the mean residence time for carbon in the system.

In principle, even though $\bar{t}$ for energy is not a measurable quantity, it can be calculated from a detailed kinetic analysis of the system. For any real system the complexity makes this impossible, and we can only note that the quantity is related to the sum of the average relaxation times for all of the processes between the initial reaction leading to energy absorption and the final dissipation of energy by heat flow to the sink.

We can, in fact, calculate the actual $\bar{t}$ for carbon in the earth's biosphere from Eq. (3-13) and examine the consequence of this value in terms of energy flux. First, we need to consider the size of the various carbon pools on the surface of the earth. This is given in Table 3-9, taken from

TABLE 3-9

DISTRIBUTION OF TERRESTRIAL CARBON

Compartment	Total carbon on earth $\times 10^{-18}$ gm
Carbonate in sediment	67,000
Organic carbon in sediment	25,000
CO_2 in the atmosphere	2.35
Living matter on land	0.3
Dead organic matter on land	2.6
CO_2 as H_2CO_3 in ocean	0.8
CO_2 as HCO_3^- in ocean	114.7
CO_2 as CO_3^{--} in ocean	14.2
Dead organic matter in ocean	10.0
Living organic matter in ocean	0.03

the paper of Revelle and Suess (57) who gathered the data from a number of other authors (58–60). These data can be used to obtain the right-hand side of Eq. (3-13).

The flow data obtained from Hutchinson (58) is:

(a) total CO_2 fixed per annum on land by photosynthesis, $0.073 \pm 0.018 \times 10^{18}$ gm;

(b) total CO_2 fixed per annum in oceans by photosynthesis, $0.43 \pm 0.3 \times 10^{18}$ gm.

We can thus compute two carbon-residence times, terrestrial and oceanic, by taking the total terrestrial biomass (living and dead) and the total oceanic biomass which are 2.9×10^{18} gm and 10.03×10^{18} gm, respectively. The corresponding residence times are 40 years and 21.8 years. An average flow of 0.003 eV per atom of biomass per year is sufficient to maintain the energy level of the biomass. This flow would correspond to a total annual flow of energy through the biosphere of 4.8×10^{17} kcal, a figure in surprisingly good agreement with Rabir owitch's estimate (61) of $13.6 \pm 8.1 \times 10^{17}$ kcal as the yearly fixation of energy by photosynthesis.

Returning to the bond distribution method, one further approach to certain nonequilibrium problems has recently been investigated (50). Since very preliminary work is available, we will only briefly discuss the technique. If we consider a steady state system maintained by an energy flux, we may inquire into the distribution of chemical species. The answer to this problem is found in a very complex kinetic analysis where the modes of energy flow must be spelled out in great detail. Consider, however, a subclass of steady states in which the energy is a certain increment ϵ above the ground state and is distributed in a random way among available bond types. We may then attempt to determine the most probable distribution of this energy among the bonds. This cannot, at the moment, be done analytically, but may be approached by a computer program. We are thus able to define one class of steady states which can be investigated independently of the kinetic details of the system.

The combination of the energy flow thesis with the bond energy approach enables us to discuss a whole series of experiments in a rather unified way. These experiments have been motivated by attempts to show how prebiological synthesis of small organic molecules could have taken place. In all of these experiments, one starts with simple mixtures of molecules such as H_2O, CO_2, N_2, NH_3, CH_4, etc. The system is then subjected to a high potential source of energy such as ionizing radiation, ultraviolet light, a high temperature reservoir, or a continuous spark discharge. In general, there is an energy sink in the form of a water jacket or the surroundings. Thus, the system maintains a flux of energy from a source to a sink. In most such experiments there is no indication that a steady state is reached; however, during the energy flux the potential energy of the system must be above that of the ground state for the appropriate temperature and atomic composition. Experiments of this type are extensively reviewed in the three compendia edited by Clark and Synge (51), Fox (52), and Shneour and Ottensen (53).

Under reducing conditions, high yields of amino acids, hydroxyacids, and one- and two-carbon intermediates are produced. In addition, monosaccharides, purines, purine intermediates, and pyrimidines have been reported (54). A detailed analysis of the reaction products reported shows surprising similarities among the experiments in spite of the wide diversity of energy fluxes, boundary conditions, and starting materials. This similarity is partially due to the methods of assay (amino acid chromatography and ninhydrin analysis are almost universal techniques in biochemistry laboratories) and partially due to more fundamental reasons.

If we return to Table 3-5 which is an equilibrium system composed primarily of H_2O, CO_2, N_2, and CH_4, we may ask the following question. Assuming that energy now flows through such a system so as to raise the average electronic energy, what will be the distribution of chemical species? Compounds down on the list in upper-lying energy states must be enriched at the expense of the abundant low-lying compounds. There is no alternative; if the energy is supplied in a form such that it goes into chemical bond energy, rearrangements must occur, leading to different bonds and different small molecules. The particular molecules that emerge depend on the starting materials and the methods of energy supply, but certain stable intermediate species will predominate in any type of random synthesis in which the right atoms are available.

Thus, starting with an equilibrium system of the proper atomic composition, energy flux will produce small organic molecules. All one- and two-carbon compounds with nitrogen, hydrogen, and oxygen must be regarded as potential precursors to biological synthesis. Hence, these experiments, as detailed models of prebiology, must be interpreted with caution and within the general framework of energy flow rather than as sufficient justification for certain specific theories of the nature of the prebiological earth. They do show certain favored compounds emerging under energy flux, but they cannot in themselves argue as to which flow was operative in producing terrestrial prebiological molecules. The demonstration that a particular molecule can be produced under energy flux is no longer sufficient to argue the role of that molecule in prebiology. After all, we are now convinced that with sufficient expenditure of energy, any small organic compound can be synthesized in the laboratory. Indeed, if we are willing to settle for sufficiently low yields, any small organic molecule can be synthesized randomly in the laboratory without excessive effort on the part of the experimenter.

Thus far in this chapter we have concentrated attention on relevant chemical species. The forms of energy input constitute the second aspect of the general problem and are now considered. First, we examine the actual energy flows operative on the surface of our planet at the present. These data have been summarized by Miller and Urey (55) and are given in Table 3-10.

TABLE 3-10

TERRESTRIAL ENERGY SOURCES[a]

Source	Energy (cal/cm²/year)
Sunlight (all wavelengths)	260,000
< 2500 Å	570
< 2000 Å	85
< 1500 Å	3.5
Electric discharges	4
Cosmic rays	0.0015
Radioactivity (to 1.0 km depth)	0.8
Volcanoes	0.13

[a] Miller and Urey (55).

These data make it clear that in recent geological epochs, solar energy must be the dominant energy flux for biological organization. There would thus seem to be strong reason for using an energy distribution analogous to the solar spectrum in abiotic synthesis experiments. Not only is solar flux by far the largest contributor to the energy, but it is clearly the organizing factor for present-day ecology (we will return to this idea in Chapter V).

These ideas have been clearly formulated by Gaffron (52) who noted: "We are agreed that radiation with light quanta of sufficient energy to break H—O or H—C bonds, or any other equivalent method of radical formation, caused or contributed to the accumulation of many moderately complex organic substances on the surface of the Earth. After listening to the reports on spontaneous chemical synthesis at this meeting it appears as if nearly all smaller organic molecules (below molecular weight 1000) which play the role of metabolic building stones and catalysts in living cell, might have arisen spontaneously and in large quantities by one way or another, and therefore, served for either biopoesis or as food for organisms intruding from outer space.

"There is no evidence, however, that a mere accumulation of low molecular weight organic material is sufficient to bring about the mysterious emergence of self reproducing entities and such an accumulation would suffice even less without a continuous influx of free energy. The only uninterrupted supply of useful energy has been daylight." Starting from a consideration of solar luminosity, Sagan (62) has presented a discussion favoring the dominant role of ultraviolet light among primitive energy sources relevant to the origin of life. He calculates that 4×10^9 years ago, the available flux of radiation shorter than 2900 Å was 7×10^{14} photons/cm^2 sec at the top of the earth's atmosphere.

One further feature distinguishes solar energy from the other possible energy sources: it has molecular specificity. That is, all molecules have well-defined absorption spectra for electromagnetic radiation in the range from 1500 Å into the microwave region. Thus, absorption of electromagnetic energy of these wavelengths by a collection of molecules is nonrandom. This is particularly true in the ultraviolet and visible range of the spectrum. The whole science of photochemistry is indeed dependent on the fact that absorption probabilities and transition probabilities are reasonably sharp functions of the spectrum of the incident radiation.

For short wavelength radiation and ionizing particles, the energy is distributed more or less randomly in the absorbers. Since the photon and particle energies are so much larger than the ionization and excitation potentials of the absorbing material, this type of energy flux depends only on the atomic composition and not the molecular details of the absorbers. No present-day methods are known for channeling this energy into biological processes in a directed way. There is no vestigal evidence that ionizing radiation ever played a role as a biological energy source.

Thermal energy tends to become distributed so rapidly among all the molecules in a collecton that very little chemical specificity can be discerned. This applies also to longer wavelength electromagnetic energy which very rapidly shows up as thermal energy, since it is absorbed directly into vibrational and rotational degrees of freedom. However, for those wavelengths that can cause electronic transitions or excitations leading to photochemical reactions, there is a profound relationship between the chemical state of the system and the spectrum of the incident radiation.

For studying this problem for the terrestrial surface, data on the energy distribution of the incident solar radiation has been collected and summarized by Johnson (56). Because of the great importance of these data in the problem of biogenesis, they are presented in detail in Appendix V. Figure 3-2 is a graph of this distribution. The general facts about the solar spectrum may be organized so as to give a better idea of the relation of various wavelength regions to specific photochemical processes. Table 3-11 presents this analysis. The distribution of the energy output of the sun is thus favorable to electronic transitions in the normal covalent chemistry of CHNOPS compounds.

Within the context of the material discussed in this chapter, we can formulate an approach to the study of the origin of life. The starting system for both theoretical and experimental analysis consists of a container having an appropriate atomic composition and subjected to a

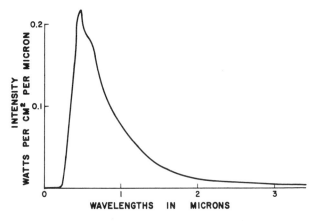

FIG. 3-2. Spectral distribution of solar energy incident on the earth's atmosphere. The geochemical, meteorological, and biochemical development of the earth's surface have been profoundly affected by this spectral distribution.

TABLE 3-11

SOLAR ENERGY DISTRIBUTION AND PHOTOCHEMISTRY

Region	Wavelength range (μ)	Energy range (kcal/Einstein)	Fraction of solar spectrum (%)	Molecular changes
Far ultraviolet	0.1–0.2	152.2–304.4	0.02	Ionization
Ultraviolet	0.2–0.38	75.3–152.2	7.27	Electronic transitions and ionizations
Visible	0.38–0.78	36.7–75.3	51.73	Electronic transitions
Near infrared	0.78–3	9.5–36.7	38.90	Electronic and vibrational transitions
Middle infrared	3–30	0.95–9.5	2.10	Rotational and vibrational transitions

flux of radiation approximating to the solar spectrum. Under these conditions, we may allow the system to age and we may ask the questions:

(1) Which compounds predominate?

(2) Which cycles predominate?

(3) Which chromophores arise in the photosynthetically induced cycles? Is there a relationship between the absorption spectrum of the chromophores synthesized and the spectral distribution of the incident radiation?

(4) How does more organized behavior come about?

At this stage, we can study the previously described system either experimentally or in terms of rather specific theoretical considerations of photochemistry, atmospheric physics, free radical reactions, hydrodynamics, etc. We have no elegant or general theory for nonequilibrium systems that can provide guidance at this time. We can, from the biological point of view, be guided by the kind of life that we know has emerged, but we must primarily gather information about a class of empirical results. The general physical chemistry of energy flow systems becomes an extremely important field of biological interest.

Our previous considerations indicate to us that organization will take place in all energy flow systems. The challenge now is to discern those features of organization that can be codified into a more general theory of life. One of the major problems in trying to analyze biology in terms of concepts of thermal physics is to account for specific molecules that occur and to provide a physically based reason for the particular choice. In addition, the emergence of membranes or the more general problem of phase separation and diffusion limitation, might be areas where a general theory should provide some insight. One further concept that should emerge from a general theory is the thermodynamic advantage of a template mechanism and the emergence of self-duplication as we now recognize it.

Our present considerations only hint at many of these problems. They do, on the other hand, strongly suggest the energy flow point of view as the conceptual framework in which to look for solutions.

References

1. J. D. Bernal, *in* "Theoretical and Mathematical Biology" (T. H. Waterman and H. J. Morowitz, eds.), Chapter 5. Random House (Blaisdell), New York, 1965.
2. H. J. Morowitz, *Arch. Biochem. Biophys.* **59**, 341 (1955).
3. G. T. Armstrong, E. S. Domalski, G. T. Furukawa, and M. A. Krivanec, Preliminary report on a survey of thermodynamic properties of the compounds of the elements CHNOPS. *Natl. Bur. Std. (U.S.) Rept.* 8521 (1964).

4. D. A. Webb and W. R. Fearon, *Sci. Proc. Roy. Dublin Soc.* **21**, 487 (1937).
5. D. Bertrand, *Bull. Am. Museum Nat. Hist.* **94**, 403 (1950).
6. W. Vernadsky, *Z. Krist. Mineral. Petrog., Abt. B Mineral. Petrog. Mitt.* **44**, 191 (1933).
7. R. B. Roberts, P. H. Abelson, D. B. Cowie, E. T. Bolton, and R. J. Britten, "Studies of Biosynthesis in *Escherichia coli.*" Publ. 607, Carnegie Inst. of Washington, Washington, D.C., 1955.
8. G. A. Knaysi, "Elements of Bacterial Cytology." Cornell Univ. Press (Comstock), Ithaca, New York, 1951.
9. M. Florkin, "Biochemical Evolution." Academic Press, New York, 1949.
10. H. W. Milner, *in* "Algal Culture from Laboratory to Pilot Plant" (J. S. Burlew, ed.). Publ. 600, Carnegie Inst. of Washington, Washington, D.C., 1953.
11. F. S. M. Grylls, *in* "Biochemists' Handbook" (C. Long, ed.). Van Nostrand, Princeton, New Jersey, 1961.
12. "The Composition of Foods." Spec. Rept. Ser. Med. Res. Com. London No. 297, 1960.
13. H. J. Morowitz, M. E. Tourtellotte, W. R. Guild, E. Castro, and C. Woese, *J. Mol. Biol.* **4**, 93 (1962).
14. M. W. Miller, "The Pfizer Handbook of Microbial Metabolites." McGraw-Hill, New York, 1961.
15. F. Turba and J. Esser, *Biochemistry* **387**, 93 (1956).
16. P. Applewhite and H. J. Morowitz, unpublished work.
17. M. Florkin and H. S. Mason, "Comparative Biochemistry." Academic Press, New York, 1960.
18. W. Karrer, "Konstitution und Vorkommen der Organischen Pflanzenstoffe." Birkhäuser, Basel, 1958.
19. B. J. Luyet and P. M. Gehenio, "Life and Death at Low Temperatures." Biodynamica, Normandy, Missouri, 1940.
20. A. I. Skoultchi and H. J. Morowitz, *Yale J. Biol. Med.* **37**, 158 (1964).
21. R. C. Tolman, "Principles of Statistical Mechanics." Oxford Univ. Press, London and New York, 1938.
22. F. Lipmann, *Advan. Enzymol.* **1**, 99 (1941).
23. H. A. Krebs and H. L. Kornberg, "Energy Transformations in Living Matter." Springer, Berlin, 1957.
24. A. L. Lehninger, "Bioenergetics." Benjamin, New York, Amsterdam, 1965.
25. J. D. Robertson, *Sci. Am.* **206**, 64 (1962).
26. H. B. Schwann and K. S. Cole, *in* "Medical Physics" (O. Glasser, ed.), 3rd ed. Year Book Publ., Chicago, Illinois, 1960.
27. E. Schrödinger, "What is Life?" Macmillan, New York, 1945.
28. M. L. Petermann, "The Physical and Chemical Properties of Ribosomes." American Elsevier, New York, 1964.
29. H. E. Suess, *J. Geophys. Res.* **67**, 2029 (1962).
30. M. O. Dayhoff, E. R. Lippincott, and R. V. Eck, *Science* **146**, 1461 (1964).
31. W. B. White, S. M. Johnson, and G. B. Dantzig, *J. Chem. Phys.* **28**, 751 (1959).
32. D. W. Van Kevelen and H. A. G. Chermin, *Chem. Eng. Sci.* **1**, 66 (1951).
33. A. I. Oparin, "The Origin of Life on Earth." Academic Press, New York, 1957.
34. G. T. Armstrong, E. S. Domalski, G. T. Furukawa, and M. A. Krivanec, *Natl. Bur. Std. (U.S.) Rept.* 8595 (1964).

35. G. T. Armstrong, E. S. Domalski, I. Halow, M. N. Inscoe, G. T. Furukawa, and M. A. Krivanec, *Natl. Bur. Std. (U.S.) Rept.* 8641 (1965).
36. G. T. Armstrong, E. S. Domalski, M. N. Inscoe, I. Halow, G. T. Furukawa, and M. K. Buresh, *Natl. Bur. Std. (U.S.) Rept.* 8906 (1965).
37. M. K. Buresh, M. L. Reilly, G. T. Furukawa, and G. T. Armstrong, *Natl. Bur. Std. (U.S.) Rept.* 8992 (1965).
38. G. T. Furukawa, M. K. Buresh, M. L. Reilly, and G. T. Armstrong, *Natl. Bur. Std. (U.S.) Rept.* 9043 (1966).
39. G. T. Furukawa, M. K. Buresh, M. L. Reilly, G. T. Armstrong, and G. D. Mitchell, *Natl. Bur. Std. (U.S.) Rept.* 9089 (1966).
40. G. T. Furukawa, M. L. Reilly, G. T. Armstrong, G. D. Mitchell, and I. Halow, *Natl. Bur. Std. (U.S.) Rept.* 9374 (1966).
41. J. P. Phelps, Ph.D. Dissertation, Yale Univ., New Haven, Connecticut, 1959.
42. V. I. Vedeneyev, L. V. Gurvich, V. N. Kondrat'yev, V. A. Medvedev, and Ye. L. Frankevich, "Bond Energies, Ionization Potentials, and Electron Affinities." St. Martin's Press, New York, 1966.
43. T. L. Cottrell, "The Strength of Chemical Bonds." Butterworth, London and Washington, D.C., 1958.
44. L. Pauling, "The Nature of the Chemical Bond." Cornell Univ. Press, Ithaca, New York, 1942.
45. M. L. Huggins, *J. Am. Chem. Soc.* 75, 4123 (1953).
46. H. J. Morowitz, Molecular physics of living cells. *In* "Medical Physics" (O. Glasser, ed.), Vol. III, p. 111. Year Book Publ., Chicago, Illinois, 1960.
47. H. J. Morowitz, *in* "Encyclopedia of the Biological Sciences" (P. Gray, ed.), p. 155. Reinhold, New York, 1961.
48. C. C. Cheng, Master's Thesis, Univ. of Connecticut, 1962.
49. H. R. Bode and H. J. Morowitz, *J. Mol. Biol.* 23, 191 (1967).
50. K. Rider and H. J. Morowitz, unpublished work.
51. F. Clark and R. L. M. Synge (eds.) "The Origin of Life on Earth." Pergamon Press, New York, 1959.
52. S. Fox (ed.), "The Origins of Prebiological Systems and of Their Molecular Matrices." Academic Press, New York, 1965.
53. E. A. Shneour and E. A. Ottensen (eds.), "Extraterrestrial Life, An Anthology and Bibliography." Natl. Acad. Sci., Washington, D.C., 1966.
54. J. Oro, *Ann. N.Y. Acad. Sci.* 108, 464 (1963).
55. S. L. Miller and H. C. Urey, *Science* 130, 245 (1959).
56. F. S. Johnson, *J. Meteorol.* 11, 431 (1954).
57. R. Revelle and H. E. Suess, *Tellus* 9, 18 (1957).
58. G. E. Hutchinson, *in* "The Earth as a Planet" (G. Kuiper, ed.), Chap. 8. Chicago Univ. Press, Chicago, Illinois, 1954.
59. W. W. Rubey, *Bull. Geol. Soc. Am.* 61, 111 (1951).
60. H. U. Sverdup, M. W. Johnson, and R. H. Flemming, "The Oceans." Prentice-Hall, Englewood Cliffs, New Jersey, 1942.
61. E. I. Rabinowitch, "Photosynthesis," Vol. I. Wiley (Interscience), New York, 1945.
62. C. Sagan, *in* "The Origins of Prebiological Systems and of Their Molecular Matrices" (S. Fox, ed.), pp. 238–239. Academic Press, New York, 1965.

IV
The Free Energy of the Biosphere

There is measure in every thing.
Shakespeare, "Much Ado About Nothing"

All depends on the measure.
"Mishna, Baba Metzia"

In previous chapters we have examined the general concept of energy flow in biology with particular attention to the problem of how organization comes about *de novo*. In this chapter we shall shift attention to an examination of present-day energy flow in existing terrestrial biology to see a functioning form of the principle.

We begin by restating the concept that biology as we know it is dependent on the earth taking in sunlight and radiating infrared energy to outer space. If we were to surround the planet with an adiabatic envelope, all living processes would cease within a short time and the system would begin to decay to some equilibrium state. Solar energy influx is clearly necessary for the maintenance of life. It is just as necessary that a sink be provided for the outflow of thermal energy. If this were not so, the planet would continuously heat up and life would again soon cease to exist. All biological processes depend on the absorption of solar photons and the transfer of heat to celestial sinks.

This principle has been elegantly stated by Albert Szent-Györgi (*1*) who wrote, "It is common knowledge that the ultimate source of all our energy and negative entropy is the radiation of the sun. When a photon interacts with a material particle on our globe it lifts one electron from an electron pair to a higher level. This excited state as a rule has but a short lifetime and the electron drops back within 10^{-7} to 10^{-8} seconds to the ground state giving off its excess energy in one way or another. Life has learned to catch the electron in the excited state, uncouple it from its partner and let it drop back to the ground state through its biological machinery utilizing its excess energy for life processes."

At the risk of repetition, some stress is necessary on the role of the sink in the functioning of the biosphere. The sun would not be a source of "negentropy" if there were not a sink for the flow of thermal energy. The surface of the earth does not gain net energy from the sun but remains at a constant total energy, reradiating as much energy as is taken up. The subtle difference is that it is not energy *per se* that makes life go, but the flow of energy through the system. The importance of considering energy flow in biological processes is the central theme of this book. The concept of flow of energy gives us a powerful basis for physical analysis of the system as we have seen in Chapters I and II and will be elaborated in Chapter VI.

We have already proven that energy flow leads to cyclic processes. The existence of flows of this type is as much a feature of geology and meteorology as it is of biology. In geology the energy sources are more complex, consisting of (a) solar radiation, (b) mechanical energy both from gravitational processes on the earth as well as gravitational processes in the solar system such as tides, (c) chemical free energy stored in geological deposits which are above the lowest energy state, (d) nuclear energy, and (e) available thermal energy from the hot core of the earth. These sources serve to drive geological processes as described by Mason (2), "We have been considering the geochemical cycle in terms of the material changes which take place during the various processes. Equally

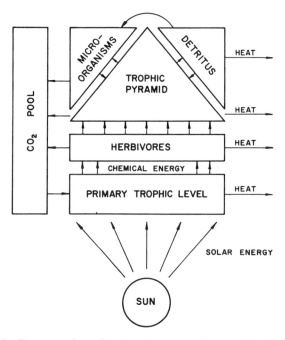

FIG. 4-1. Representation of ecology in terms of energy flux indicating that ecological processes are driven by the flow of energy from the sun to thermal sinks.

significant, if less studied and less well understood, are the energy changes during the cycle. Geochemical processes operate only because of a flow of energy from a higher to a lower potential or intensity; hence energy is no less important than matter in the geochemical cycle."

In meteorology the idealized water cycle is an example of a cyclic process driven directly by solar energy. Sunlight falling on bodies of terrestrial water causes evaporation, vaporization, and the rising of water molecules to higher altitudes. The molecules condense into liquid water giving off heat, some of which is radiated to outer space. The condensed water now has mechanical (gravitational) potential energy. The water falls back to earth in the form of rain and the potential energy is converted to heat, some of which is radiated to outer space. The water thus cycles between terrestrial water and clouds. The process depends on the flow of energy from the sun through the earth's surface to outer space. The process is a thermomechanical analog of the various biological cycles, and indeed closely relates to them since life as we know it is intimately connected to the supply of water. This analogy between the water cycle and cycles of living systems has been pointed out by Fritz Lipmann (3).

The global ecological system, the biosphere, can then be defined as that part of the terrestrial surface which is ordered by the flow of energy, mediated by photosynthetic processes. The importance of energy flow has long been recognized by ecologists to be the vital step in organizing the ecosystem. Raymond L. Lindeman in his classical paper (4) stated that, "The basic process in trophic dynamics is the transfer of energy from one part of the ecosystem to another." The entire trophic concept can be formulated in energetic terms as is shown in Fig. 4-1. Energy enters the system as photons and is transformed into energetic covalent bonds. All subsequent biochemical changes involve a series of rearrangements which are accompanied by the production of heat. We shall later demonstrate the internal necessity of this heat loss in terms of entropic considerations. The energy outflow is usually accompanied by the loss of CO_2, water, and nitrogenous compounds. This material then moves through the well-known cycles and eventually back into the biosphere.

The analysis of a number of macroscopic aspects of ecology in terms of energy transfer has recently been undertaken by Gates (5). His book is an example of attempts to analyze biological phenomena in terms of thermodynamic concepts.

For a more detailed understanding of the significance of the flux of energy in the present biosphere, we must examine the actual enthalpy and entropy changes occurring in various biological transformations. These processes can all be encompassed in the scheme involving the synthesis of biomass from the simplest and lowest energy precursors. The model process we shall study is given in the following idealized reaction sequence,

$$CO_2 + N_2 + H_2O + H_2SO_4 + H_3PO_4 \rightarrow \text{Biomass} + O_2 \qquad (4\text{-}1)$$

Equation (4-1) might at first be regarded as an abstract relation for idealized cycles of carbon and nitrogen. On the other hand, there are living organisms for which this equation is a fairly precise representation of the overall cell growth. Consider, for example, the blue-green algae, phylum Cyanophyta. In the order Nostocinales there are a number of species which are both photosynthetic and fixers of free nitrogen (6, 7). They are mostly included in the genera *Anabaena*, *Cylindrospermum*, *Nostoc*, and *Mastigocladus*. Equation (4-1) is of course incomplete for these organisms in that we have ignored the sodium, potassium, magnesium, manganese, molybdenum, cobalt, and other trace substances. However, from a bulk thermodynamic point of view, the relation approximately describes the overall processes for these extremely versatile cells. The genomes of these procaryotic cells are required to encode sufficient information to generate enzymes to carry out the entire metabolic chart.

A number of other reaction sequences closely related to Eq. (4-1) might be studied by using the same methods of analysis. Three of these are:

$$CO_2 + HNO_3 + H_2O + H_2SO_4 + H_3PO_4 \rightarrow \text{Biomass} + O_2 \qquad (4\text{-}2)$$

$$CO_2 + NH_3 + H_2O + H_2SO_4 + H_3PO_4 \rightarrow \text{Biomass} + O_2 \qquad (4\text{-}3)$$

$$C_6H_{12}O_6 + NH_3 + H_2SO_4 + H_3PO_4 \rightarrow \text{Biomass} + CO_2 + H_2O \qquad (4\text{-}4)$$

Equations (4-2) and (4-3) are representative of the growth of photosynthetic organisms or symbiotic associations of photosynthesizers with nitrogen reducers. Equation (4-4) is representative of the anaerobic growth of a biochemically versatile bacterium such as *Escherichia coli* on a minimal medium (8, 9).

We will examine the model processes with respect to various changes in entropy, enthalpy, and free energy. In the course of this analysis, we will find that much of the necessary experimental data is unavailable and in other cases, only approximate values exist. In these cases we will use the best available methods which can be employed to estimate the thermodynamic parameters from a knowledge of molecular structure and group contributions. In spite of the limitations we will be able to gain some useful insights into the thermodynamic changes in the major biological cycles, in cell replication, and in the transfer of biomass between trophic levels. This chapter represents a first attempt at total thermodynamic bookkeeping in existing biological systems.

To begin our analysis we must consider the concept of biomass in more concrete biochemical terms. If we know the composition of a living organism in terms of the major components—proteins, nucleic acids, fats, and carbohydrates—we can then use this information to deduce the distribution of monomers and small components. However, this figure varies widely from some adult plants, which are almost entirely carbohydrate, to some fish which are primarily protein and fat and contain almost no carbohydrate. (This problem was discussed in Chapter III and some of the available data reviewed in Table 3-3.) Microorganisms have a considerably higher proportion of their mass in nucleic acids.

In choosing an appropriate distribution to carry out our biomass calculation, we will use compositional data from bacteria. This is somewhat arbitrary, but microorganisms represent a large fraction of the total biomass and are ubiquitously distributed. The calculations we are outlining could be carried out for any macromolecular composition and it is clear that for a detailed view of energetics in general ecology, it will be profitable to examine the free energy of formation for each trophic level. We will return to such considerations in Chapter V.

For present considerations, biomass as used in Eqs. (4-1)–(4-4) is high polymer material having the monomeric composition shown in Table 4-1. In this table we also indicate the number of moles of each constituent necessary to make one gram dry weight of biomass. Utilizing the atomic composition of the components, we can write balanced equations and calculate the amounts of starting material required for the cases represented by Eqs. (4-1)–(4-4). The entire analysis must be carried out stepwise to best utilize the currently available thermochemical data on compounds of interest. The first step of the calculation does not represent complete synthesis of biomass, but the synthesis of low molecular weight precursors. Table 4-2 represents the balanced equations for the synthesis of enough precursors to make one gram of biomass.

In cases I–III (to be presented), oxygen occurs in the products in order to maintain mass balance. The production of oxygen in these cases is also predictable from the general features of the carbon cycle involving the reduction of water in the formation of carbohydrates. Another way of viewing the situation is to note that the precursors are in a highly oxidized state with respect to the final biomass. This accords with the general notion that the synthesis of biological compounds could have proceeded much more easily in a reducing environment. In case IV, CO_2 and water occur in the products in order to maintain mass balance. Table 4-2 is equivalent to writing Eqs. (4-1)–(4-4) in stoichiometric form, which we proceed to do in the case of (4-1). All coefficients are

TABLE 4-1

CHEMICAL COMPOSITION OF DRY BIOMASS

Compound	Mole fraction in dry material	Moles/gm dry biomass × 10^4
Alanine	0.0552	4.54
Arginine	0.0306	2.52
Aspartic acid	0.0245	2.01
Asparagine	0.0123	1.01
Cysteine	0.0123	1.01
Glutamic acid	0.0429	3.53
Glutamine	0.0245	2.01
Glycine	0.0490	4.03
Histidine	0.0061	0.50
Isoleucine	0.0306	2.52
Leucine	0.0490	4.03
Lysine	0.0490	4.03
Methionine	0.0245	2.01
Phenylalanine	0.0184	1.51
Proline	0.0306	2.52
Serine	0.0368	3.02
Threonine	0.0303	2.52
Tryptophan	0.0061	0.50
Tyrosine	0.0122	1.01
Valine	0.0369	3.02
Hexose	0.1249	10.26
Ribose	0.0544	4.47
Deoxyribose	0.0117	0.96
Thymine	0.0029	0.24
Adenine	0.0170	1.40
Guanine	0.0170	1.40
Cystosine	0.0170	1.40
Uracil	0.0140	1.15
Glycerin	0.0170	1.40
Fatty acid	0.0340	2.80
Phosphate	0.0830	6.80
Other	0.0253	2.08

multiplied by 10^4 to avoid negative exponents on the left-hand side of the equation:

$$(410.35)CO_2 + (46.64)N_2 + (398.20)H_2O$$
$$+ (3.0)H_2SO_4 + (6.8)H_3PO_4 \rightarrow (506.60)O_2 + 10^4 \text{ gm Biomass} \quad (4\text{-}5)$$

TABLE 4-2

MASS BALANCE IN THE SYNTHESIS OF PRECURSORS OF BIOMASS

	Eq. (4-1), moles × 10⁴	Eq. (4-2), moles × 10⁴	Eq. (4-3), moles × 10⁴	Eq. (4-4), moles × 10⁴
Reactants				
CO_2	410.35	410.35	410.35	
$C_6H_{12}O_6$				71.98
N_2	46.64			
HNO_3		93.28		
NH_3			93.28	93.28
H_2O	398.20	356.55	263.77	
H_2SO_4	3.0	3.0	3.0	3.0
H_3PO_4	6.8	6.8	6.8	6.8
Products				
O_2	506.60	620.69	434.38	
CO_2				25.53
H_2O				173.11
Biomass precursors	Sufficient material to synthesize one gram of biomass			

We may now proceed to the calculation of the heats of formation and the entropies of the reactants. In principle we start with the elements in their standard states and determine the heats of formation and the entropies of the compounds in their standard states. We then consider the thermodynamic changes in going from the pure components to a dilute aqueous solution. This involves a specification of the final volume of the solution, as the entropy of solution is a function of the concentration. In practice much of the thermodynamic data of the reactants is available for compounds in aqueous solution, which is taken to be the hypothetical state of unit molarity and unit activity coefficient. That is, the data are calculated for materials at unit molarity which behave as if they were at infinite dilution. The heats of formation are thus those for infinite dilution and may be used directly. The total entropy must be determined from the tabulated entropies at unit molarity plus the entropy of dilution plus the entropy of mixing. As noted, the entropy calculation depends on the volume of the solution so that volume will be carried as a parameter in the calculations.

The starting states will then be considered as:

Case I. A dilute aqueous solution of sulfuric acid and phosphoric acid along with a container of nitrogen gas and carbon dioxide at 1 atm. The entire system is at 25°C.

Case II. A dilute aqueous solution of nitric acid, sulfuric acid, and phosphoric acid at 25°C, along with a container of carbon dioxide at 1 atm.

Case III. A dilute aqueous solution of carbon dioxide, ammonia, sulfuric acid, and phosphoric acid at 25°C, along with a container of carbon dioxide at 1 atm.

Case IV. A dilute solution of glucose, ammonia, sulfuric acid, and phosphoric acid at 25°C.

The entropy of dilution is given by

$$\Delta S_d = -R \sum_i n_i \ln(n_i/V) \tag{4-6}$$

where n_i is the number of moles of the ith substance and V is the final volume of the system. The entropy of mixing is given by

$$\Delta S_m = -R \sum_i n_i \ln(n_i/\sum n_i) \tag{4-7}$$

for both the liquid and gas mixtures. Their sum is

$$\Delta S_d + \Delta S_m = R \ln V \sum_i n_i - R \sum_i n_i \ln(n_i^2/\sum n_i) \tag{4-8}$$

Note that in calculating these entropies, we do not include the water since we are in dilute aqueous solution. The relevant thermodynamic data are given in Tables 4-3 and 4-4. We may now utilize Tables 4-2 to 4-4 and Eq. (4-8) to calculate the standard heats of formation and entropies of the starting materials. The results of these calculations are shown in Table 4-5.

The product of the first stage of the reaction will be a dilute solution of all the components listed in Table 4-1, at a temperature of 25°C. In addition, cases I–III will give rise to free oxygen gas at a pressure of 1 atm and a temperature of 25°C. In case IV the final mixture will be accompanied by free carbon dioxide gas at 1 atm. The next group of values required will then be the heats of formation, entropies, heats of solution, and entropies of solution of all the product molecules.

The primary data for this calculation are given in Table 4-6. The heat of formation of each component in the mixture can be obtained by adding the heat of formation of the crystal to the heat of solution at infinite

TABLE 4-3

Thermodynamic Constants of Reactants

Compound	Standard heat of formation in aqueous soln. (kcal/mole)	Entropy in aqueous soln. (cal/mole °C)	Ref.
$C_6H_{12}O_6$	−301.63	63.1	11, 37
H_2O	−68.32	16.72	10
HNO_3	−49.37	35.0	10
NH_3	−19.32	26.3	10
H_3PO_4	−308.20	42.1	12
H_2SO_4	−216.90	4.1	10

TABLE 4-4

Thermodynamic Constants of Gaseous Components

Substance	Standard heat of formation in gas phase (kcal/mole)	Entropy in gas phase (cal/mole °C)
O_2	—	49.003
N_2	—	45.77
CO_2	−94.05	51.06

TABLE 4-5

Heats of Formation and Entropies of Reaction Mixtures

Case	Heat of formation (kcal/gm)	Entropy (cal/gm °C)
I	−6.769	$3.050 + 0.002 \ln V$
II	−7.006	$3.156 + 0.020 \ln V$
III	−6.009	$2.920 + 0.020 \ln V$
IV	−2.608	$0.931 + 0.035 \ln V$

TABLE 4-6

THERMODYNAMIC CONSTANTS OF THE SMALL MOLECULAR WEIGHT CONSTITUENTS OF BIOMASS

Compound	Heat of formation (kcal/mole)	Entropy (cal/mole °C)	Heat of soln., infinite dilution (kcal/mole)	Heat of soln., saturation (kcal/mole)	Solubility (moles/liter)
Alanine	−133.96 (13)	30.883 (21)	2.04 (35)	2.25 (35)	1.665 (41)
Arginine	−148.66 (13)	59.9 (22)	1.50 (35)	1.08 (35)	
Aspartic acid	−232.47 (13)	40.657 (23)	6.00 (35)	5.80 (35)	0.038 (41)
Asparagine	−188.50 (13)	41.7 (11)	5.75 (35)	5.75 (35)	0.186 (42)
Cysteine	−127.2 (13)	40.6 (24)			
Glutamic acid	−240.05 (13)	44.982 (23)	6.53 (35)	6.33 (35)	0.058 (41)
Glutamine	−197.8 (13)	46.631 (23)			
Glycine	−126.22 (13)	24.763 (21)	3.75 (35)	3.35 (35)	2.900 (41)
Histidine	−54.2 (14)	52.0 (25)	3.30 (35)	3.21 (35)	0.262 (41)
Isoleucine	−151.8 (13)	49.632 (26)		0.84 (36)	0.303 (41)
Leucine	−151.9 (13)	50.598 (26)	0.78 (45)	0.84 (36)	0.181 (41)
Lysine	−162.2 (13)	49.0 (25)	−4.00 (35)	−3.50 (35)	
Methionine	−180.4 (13)	55.317 (27)	4.00 (35)	4.00 (35)	

Phenylalanine	−111.9 (13)	51.005 (20)		2.82 (36)	0.175 (41)
Proline	−125.7 (13)	32.210 (28)	0.75 (35)	0.30 (35)	6.572 (41)
Serine	−173.6 (13)	35.667 (29)	5.18 (35)	5.05 (35)	0.464 (41)
Threonine	−181.4 (13)	39.8 (25)			
Tryptophan	−99.8 (13)	59.812 (28)	1.36 (35)	1.36 (35)	0.055 (41)
Tyrosine	−163.4 (13)	51.096 (28)			0.0025 (41)
Valine	−148.2 (13)	42.719 (26)	1.43 (35)	1.73 (35)	0.740 (41)
Glucose	−304.26 (15)	50.7 (11)	2.63 (37)	2.96 (37)	3.452 (37)
Ribose	−253.9 (15)	42.3 (30)			
Deoxyribose	−214.4 (16)	42.3 (30)			0.032 (43)
Thymine	−111.9 (15)	32.8 (31)			0.0068 (43)
Adenine	+23.21 (15)	36.1 (32)			0.000033 (43)
Guanine	−43.72 (15)	38.3 (32)			0.064 (43)
Cytosine	−111 (17)	28.9 (31)			0.064 (43)
Uracil	−110.2 (18)	29.2 (31)			0.032 (43)
Glycerin	−159.160 (11)	48.87 (33)	−1.410 (38)	$\Delta S = 5.46$ (40)	—
Fatty acid	−220.5 (19)	83.74 (34)			0.0000011 (44)
Phosphate	−302.6 (20)	26.41 (20)	−2.0 (12)	$\Delta S = 15.63$ (39)	—
Other	−150	40	2.0	2.0	0.100

dilution. Thus, the sums of the first and third columns will give the heat of formation of the final mixture. The entropy of the final mixture consists of (a) the entropy of each of the crystalline components plus (b) the entropy of solution at saturation plus (c) the entropy of dilution plus (d) the entropy of mixing. The entropy of the crystalline components can be obtained by direct measurements of specific heats and is given in the second column. The entropy of solution at saturation can be obtained by noting that at equilibrium the free energy change in going from crystal to solution is zero. Since, however,

$$\Delta F_{sat} = \Delta H_{sat} - T\Delta S_{sat} = 0 \qquad (4\text{-}9)$$

we get

$$\Delta S_{sat} = \frac{\Delta H_{sat}}{T} \qquad (4\text{-}10)$$

where ΔH_{sat} is the heat of solution at saturation. The entropy of dilution is given by

$$\Delta S_d = R \sum n_i \ln\left[\frac{S_i}{(n_i/V)}\right] \qquad (4\text{-}11)$$

where S_i is the solubility of the ith component.

$$\Delta S_d = R \sum n_i \ln V$$
$$+ R \sum n_i \ln S_i - R \sum n_i \ln n_i \qquad (4\text{-}12)$$

The entropy of mixing is given by Eq. (4-7).

In cases I–III we need to add the entropy of the oxygen gas formed. In case IV we need to add the entropy of the CO_2 and the water as well as the heat of formation of these components.

A study of Table 4-6 shows that we are missing a good deal of the primary data required for an accurate calculation. However, rather than give up entirely we will proceed with a rough calculation based on the following assumptions:

(1)   The average solubility and heat of solution of the missing amino acids are the same as the amino acids reported.

(2)   The average solubility and heat of solution of the missing sugars are the same as for glucose.

(3)   The average free energy of solution of the purines and pyrimidines is 6.3 kcal/mole based on the xanthine value (46, 47). We arbitrarily assume that this is half ΔH and half $T\Delta S$.

(4)   For stearic acid we assume a ΔF of solution of 9.2 kcal/mole

based on extrapolation of values for smaller carboxylic acids. We arbitrarily assume that this is half ΔH and half $T\Delta S$.

When all these factors are included and the appropriate calculations carried out, results obtained are shown in Table 4-7. Scott (54) has carried out a calculation closely related to case II, but using more approximate data for the intermediates. He obtained a value for the heat of formation of -1.855 kcal/gm.

TABLE 4-7

HEATS OF FORMATION AND ENTROPIES OF THE INTERMEDIATE SYSTEM

Case	Heat of formation (kcal/gm)	Entropy (cal/gm °C)
I	-1.5550	$2.839 + 0.0163 \ln V$
II	-1.5550	$3.581 + 0.0163 \ln V$
III	-1.5550	$2.6684 + 0.0163 \ln V$
IV	-2.9777	$0.9266 + 0.0163 \ln V$

The large number of missing data in Table 4-6 as well as the uncertain quality of a number of the reported values argues in favor of increased emphasis on experimental thermochemistry of compounds of biological interest. Thermochemistry will probably become an increasingly important part of ecology. The occasional combustion calorimeter found among ecologists is going to have to be supplemented with equipment to measure heat capacity and heats of solution.

The next stage in the present calculation involves the condensation of monomers into biomass. This can be represented schematically as

$$4.54 \times 10^{-4} \; M \; \text{Alanine}$$
$$2.52 \times 10^{-4} \; M \; \text{Arginine}$$
$$\vdots$$
$$\rightarrow 1 \; \text{gm Biomass} + 82.2 \times 10^{-4} \; M \; H_2O \qquad (4\text{-}13)$$

In carrying out the calculation in this way we have grouped two steps into one. The steps are the condensation of monomers into macromolecules (proteins, polysaccharides, nucleic acids) in dilute solution and the assembly of macromolecules into cellular structure. The reason for grouping the two steps together is our lack of sufficient information to carry out the more detailed computation.

Lacking sufficient experimental data, we treat biomass as one gigantic macromolecule and consider the free energy changes in its synthesis. The general reaction scheme we are considering is a series of polymerization steps of the following type:

$$HM_1OH + HM_2OH \rightarrow HM_1 - M_2OH + H_2O \qquad (4\text{-}14)$$

where HM_1OH and HM_2OH represent generalized monomers. The overall process is

$$\sum n_i(HM_iOH) \rightarrow Biomass + (\sum n_i)H_2O \qquad (4\text{-}15)$$

The entropy change in this type of process can be estimated by using methods of polymer statistics. If we can then assign an average value to the ΔH for polymer bond formation, we can examine the overall free energy changes in biomass synthesis.

The model system for computing the entropy change starts with a volume V in which there are M dissolved monomer molecules of average volume v. We divide the large volume into $N = V/v$ compartments or subvolumes. In the monomer state the molecules may be distributed among the subvolumes in the following number of ways

$$\frac{N!}{\prod_i n_i(N - n)!} \qquad (4\text{-}16)$$

where $n = \sum n_i$ and n_i is the number of monomer molecules of ith species.

If there are x possible orientations for each monomer, then the total number of configurations W' is given by

$$W' = \frac{N!x^n}{\prod_i n_i!(N - n)!} \qquad (4\text{-}17)$$

W' is the thermodynamic probability in the Boltzmann sense. If all the molecules are condensed into biomass, the number of possible orientations is reduced to Ny^n where y is the number of possible configurations of the monomer in the final structure. This assumes that the structure of the nonaqueous portion of the biomass is completely fixed. Each monomer is assumed to occupy a fixed place and is capable only of internal degrees of freedom such as vibrations and rotations and is not capable of independent translation. While this involves a slight degree of overspecification, it does reflect the very high degree of organization which is characteristic of all biological systems. Under these assumptions the change in entropy in going from the monomers to the biological structure is given by

$$\Delta S = k \ln Ny^n - k \ln\left[\frac{N!x^n}{\prod_i n_i!(N - n)!}\right] \qquad (4\text{-}18)$$

Applying Stirling's approximation ($\ln r! \cong r \ln r - r$), we get

$$\Delta S = -kn \ln\left(\frac{Nxe}{y}\right) + k \sum n_i \ln n_i \qquad (4\text{-}19)$$

For each species of molecule we can define a mole fraction in the biomass as

$$z_i = \frac{n_i}{n} \qquad (4\text{-}20)$$

Recasting the equation in terms of z_i we get

$$\Delta S = -kn \ln\left[\left(\frac{N}{n}\right)\left(\frac{x}{y}\right)e\right] - \sum z_i \ln z_i \qquad (4\text{-}21)$$

The ratio N/n is the number of sites associated with one molecule of monomer in solution. Since $N = V/\bar{v}$, then

$$\frac{N}{n} = \frac{V}{n\bar{v}} = \frac{V}{\sum n_i \bar{V}_i} \qquad (4\text{-}22)$$

where $\bar{V}_i$ is the partial molecular volume of the ith species. The ratio N/n can then be computed from experimental data and is equal to $V/0.000802$.

The quantity x/y is the most difficult part of Eq. (4-21) to estimate. It is the ratio of the number of possible orientations of the free monomer compared with the number of orientations in the final biological structure. The change of entropy should be approximated by that calculated for the loss of one degree of rotational freedom. Thus, using the theory of the rigid rotator, we get for one mole

$$\Delta S = R \ln\left(\frac{x}{y}\right)$$
$$\cong R\left(1 + \ln\left[\frac{8\pi^2 IkT}{h^2}\right]\right) \qquad (4\text{-}23)$$

where I is the moment of inertia of the molecule. For an average molecule of the size indicated above, the entropy contribution from restricted rotation can be estimated at $8.05\,R$ entropy units per mole at 25°C.

Table 4-8 sums up the various entropy contributions for the choice of monomers indicated previously. These results substituted in Eq. (4-21) provide our first estimate of the entropy of formation of biomass.* This

* A recent monograph by F. Gorski (50) has extensively reviewed the entropy changes in the growth of plants. Gorski discusses in detail the use of the entropy concept in biology. Extensive numerical data are given along with thermodynamic calculations.

first estimate is too large since it neglects the positive contribution due to the production of 82.2×10^{-4} moles of water in the process. The molar entropy of water at 25°C is 16.72. However, inclusion of this entire quantity ignores the hydration of the biological structures which reduces the entropy of the water. A compromise will be made by using 13.00 as the positive contribution of the water. This figure is based on -3.72 entropy units as an average entropy value for hydration of one mole of

TABLE 4-8
ENTROPY CHANGES IN MACROMOLECULE FORMATION

Term	Value
$\ln \dfrac{N}{n} = \ln\left(\dfrac{V}{\Sigma \, n_i \bar{V}_i}\right)$	$\ln V + 7.1284$ (V in liters)
$\ln \dfrac{x}{y}$	8.05
$\ln e$	1.000
$-\Sigma \, z_i \ln z_i$	3.2012
Sum	$19.3796 + \ln V$
$R \times$ sum $-$ water correction	$1.987 \ln V + 25.507$
$\Delta S = n \times$ molar entropy	$0.2097 + 0.0163 \ln V$

water per 100 gm of protein. The data on which this is based are given by Davis and McLaren (48), and the general problem of hydration of proteins is discussed by Eley and Leslie (49). The data do not admit the precision indicated by the three significant figures (3.72) and the exact value chosen is for convenience. It does indicate the appropriate order of magnitude for the hydration correction.

Having calculated the entropy change involved in structure formation we must now examine the enthalpy change. Four types of bonds are principally involved in the formation of biomass from monomeric units: (a) peptide bonds, (b) glucosidic linkages, (c) esters of fatty acids and glycerol, and (d) sugar phosphate bonds. The reactions may be represented as shown in Table 4-9. Using the concept of bond energies as elaborated in Chapter III, we would expect the enthalpies of formation of the four types of bonds to be (a) 4.7, (b) 0.0, (c) 0.0, and (d) 0.0 kcal/ mole. More experimental evidence exists on these energies. A summary of the data on peptide bonds is contained in a review article by Sturtevant (51) and is given in Table 4-10. Values are available for the free energy of hydrolysis of a number of sugar phosphate bonds as reported by

TABLE 4-9
BOND CHANGES IN POLYMER FORMATION

	Bonds broken		Bonds formed	
(a)	C—O	H—N	O—H	C—N
(b)	O—H	C—O	C—O	O—H
(c)	C—O	O—H	C—O	O—H
(d)	P—O	O—H	O—H	P—O

(a) Peptide bond formation:

$$R_1\text{—CH—C—OH} + \text{H—N—CH—C—OH} \longrightarrow \text{H}_2\text{N—CH—C—N—CH—C—OH} + \text{H}_2\text{O}$$

(b) Glycosidic bond formation (two sugar rings) $\longrightarrow$ disaccharide $+ \text{H}_2\text{O}$

(c) Ester bond formation:

$$\text{O=C—O—(CH}_2)_n\text{CH}_3 \;+\; \text{glycerol} \longrightarrow \text{ester} + \text{H}_2\text{O}$$

(d) Phosphodiester bond formation:

$$\text{Base—Sugar—O—P—O—... } \longrightarrow \text{Base—Sugar—O—P—OH} + \text{H}_2\text{O}$$

TABLE 4-10

ENTHALPY CHANGES IN THE HYDROLYSIS OF PEPTIDE BONDS[a]

Peptide	Bond hydrolyzed	ΔH (cal/mole)
Benzoyl-L-tyrosylglycinamide	Tyrosine—glycine	-1550 ± 150
Benzoyl-L-tyrosylglycine	Tyrosine—glycine	-1335 ± 90
Carbobenzoxyglycyl-L-leucine	Glycine—leucine	-2110 ± 50
Poly-L-lysine	Lysine—lysine	-1240
Carbobenzoxyglycyl-L-phenylalanine	Glycine—phenylalanine	-2550 ± 50
L-Tyrosylglycinamide	Tyrosine—glycine	-1300 ± 150

[a] From Sturtevant (51).

Meyerhof and Green (52) and Meyerhof and Oesper (53); these are given in Table 4-11.

Krebs and Kornberg (54) quote the following values, "The free energy of hydrolysis of the glucosidic bonds of starch or glycogen is about 4.3 kg cal, of the peptide bonds of the order of 3.0 kg cal and of an ester of the order of 2.5 kg cal, per mole." These free energies contain both enthalpy and entropy terms so that the enthalpy changes can be expected to be of a smaller magnitude than the Gibbs free energy changes.

TABLE 4-11

GIBBS FREE ENERGY OF HYDROLYSIS OF SUGAR—PHOSPHATE BONDS[a]

Compound	ΔF_0 (kcal/mole)	Compound	ΔF_0 (kcal/mole)
Glucose-6-phosphate	-3.0	Fructose-1-phosphate	-2.8
Galactose-6-phosphate	-3.0	Mannose-6-phosphate	-2.7
Fructose-6-phosphate	-3.0	3-Phosphoglyceric acid	-3.0
Glucose-1-phosphate	-4.9	2-Phosphoglyceric acid	-4.1

[a] Meyerhof and Green (52); Meyerhof and Oesper (53).

Considering this data we see that in most biological polymers, ΔH for synthesis probably ranges between 0 and 3000 cal/mole. We will take an assumed figure of 2000 cal/mole as a basis of calculation. At this point, it is well to note that the calculations cannot, at present, be very exact but are nonetheless significant in establishing the magnitude of quantities which are important in studying energy exchanges in the biosphere. These approximations must eventually be replaced by more exact data based on calorimetric measurements on biological material. The value of 2000 cal/mole of monomer leads to a ΔH for biomass formation of 0.0164 kcal/gm. The final free energy changes in the formation of biomass are shown in Table 4-12.

TABLE 4-12

FREE ENERGY OF FORMATION OF 1 gm OF BIOMASS

Case	ΔH (kcal/gm)	ΔS (cal/gm °C)	ΔF ($T = 298.1$°C, $V = 1$ liter) (kcal/gm)
I	5.354	$-0.421-0.002 \ln V$	5.357
II	5.468	$0.215-0.020 \ln V$	5.404
III	4.474	$-0.462-0.020 \ln V$	4.609
IV	-0.353	$-0.214-0.035 \ln V$	-0.289

In Table 4-12 two points require elaboration. In case II the entropy change is positive and in case IV the Gibbs free energy change is negative. The first situation arises from the fact that we are considering an overall process which includes considerable gas production as well as biomass formation. In case II large amounts of oxygen gas are made from dissolved nitrate and water. These are highly exentropic processes and lead to an overall entropy increase. Correspondingly, the enthalpy change is very large for this case, since the reactants are in a highly oxidized state which, in general, corresponds to large negative free energy of formation. However, if we were just to consider the entropy change in forming biomass, independently of the large contribution from the oxygen gas, then we would get a very definitely negative value. In case IV it is apparent that a biomass, CO_2, water mixture is more thermodynamically likely than a solution of glucose, ammonia, sulfate, and phosphate. While this may seem strange at first, it accords with the experimental result that if such a solution were isolated in contact with an isothermal reservoir and seeded with an anaerobic bacterium, it would be converted into biomass with a net increase of entropy of the universe.

We may now reexamine in a more precise way the problem of the spontaneous formation of a living system by a fluctuation in an equilibrium ensemble. The probability will be

$$p_L = e^{(-\Delta F/kT)} \tag{4-24}$$

For case I, starting with N_2, CO_2, H_2O, H_3PO_4, H_2SO_4 in one liter of solution, ΔF_g for one gram of material is:

$$\Delta F_g = \Delta H - T\Delta S$$

$$= 5.231 - \frac{T(-0.431)}{1000} \quad \text{kcal/gm} \quad (4\text{-}25)$$

For a cell of mass m, the free energy change is $m\Delta F_g$. Thus, in Table 4-13, we examine $p_{L\,max}$ as a function of the size of the biological structure.

TABLE 4-13

PROBABILITY OF BIOMASS ARISING AS A SPONTANEOUS FLUCTUATION
IN AN EQUILIBRIUM SYSTEM[a]

Cell mass (gm)	Maximum probability of forming a living cell
10^{-10}	$10^{-2.4 \times 10^{14}}$
10^{-11}	$10^{-2.4 \times 10^{13}}$
10^{-12}	$10^{-2.4 \times 10^{12}}$
10^{-13}	$10^{-2.4 \times 10^{11}}$
10^{-14}	$10^{-2.4 \times 10^{10}}$

[a] Calculated from thermodynamic data for varying size systems.

We have not, however, done the calculation so as to ask exactly the same question that was raised in Chapter III. To perform that calculation we must go back to Table 4-1, remove the oxygen produced from the precursors, and allow the remaining atoms to be in their lowest free energy state. This condition is met by starting with 195.7×10^{-4} moles of H_2O, 46.64×10^{-4} moles of N_2, 101.25×10^{-4} moles of CH_4, and 309.10 moles of carbon as graphite. This leads to a ΔF_g for biomass formation of 344 cal/gm, resulting in a probability of $10^{-2 \times 10^{11}}$ for a cellular structure of 10^{-12} gm, which is in fair agreement with the calculated value for $E.$ $coli$ in Table 3-9.

We may now, however, proceed to ask a more realistic question. Suppose that we are given a one-liter vat containing all the monomer units necessary to make a living cell; what is the probability that a cell will form in an equilibrium ensemble? We proceed as in the previous calculations, only the ΔH and ΔS values are considerably smaller and are equal to 0.0164 kcal/gm and 0.2079 entropy units. ΔF_g is thus 78 cal/gm. The probabilities are then given in Table 4-14.

TABLE 4-14

PROBABILITY OF A CELL ARISING SPONTANEOUSLY IN AN
OCEAN OF MONOMER UNITS

Cell mass (gm)	Probability of forming
10^{-10}	$10^{-3.4 \times 10^{12}}$
10^{-11}	$10^{-3.4 \times 10^{11}}$
10^{-12}	$10^{-3.4 \times 10^{10}}$
10^{-13}	$10^{-3.4 \times 10^{9}}$
10^{-14}	$10^{-3.4 \times 10^{8}}$

The probabilities, while much larger than in the previous case, are still infinitesimally small. We can use the approach of the previous calculations in a somewhat modified form to raise the following question. Given an ocean of volume V containing precursor monomers of biomass at a concentration of 1 gm/liter, what is the largest polymer which might be formed by thermal fluctuations in one year? To carry out this type of analysis, we must first modify the entropy expression (4-18). This expresson is too specific for present purposes in that it refers to the probability of making some specific polymer, while we wish to do the calculation for any random polymer. To do this, the term $k \ln(Ny^n)$ needs to be replaced by $k \ln(Ny^n n! / \prod_i n_i!)$ since this expression counts all possible sequences. This leads to an entropy of 0.161 units and a free energy of formation of 56.6 cal/gm. The probability of a polymer of mass m occurring is then

$$p_m = \frac{V}{m} r e^{(-56.6m/kT)} \tag{4-26}$$

where V/m is the number of members of the ensemble and r is the number of configurations which will occur in one year. We assume r to be 10^{21} and will consider all probabilities over 10^{-6}. For an ocean of 10^{18} liters we get

$$-\frac{56.6(MW)}{RT} = -104 \tag{4-27}$$

where the mass is now in molecular weight units and turns out to be 1100 daltons for a system at 300°C.

In this chapter we have examined, insofar as the data have permitted, the enthalpy, entropy, and Gibbs free energy changes in biological transformations. Although inadequacies in available data as well as uncertainties in our knowledge of macromolecular chemistry do not allow us to carry out the calculations in a completely satisfactory manner, nonetheless, the equipment is at hand with which to thoroughly study the energetic and entropic bookkeeping in living cells and organisms. This chapter can only represent an early attempt at this type of detailed analysis of bioenergetics. In the following chapters we will examine certain features of ecology and biochemistry in terms of the thermochemical framework that we have established in this chapter.

References

1. A. Szent-Györgi, in "Light and Life" (W. D. McElroy and B. Glass, eds.), p. 7. Johns Hopkins Press, Baltimore, Maryland, 1961.
2. B. Mason, "Principles of Geochemistry." Wiley, New York, 1958.
3. F. A. Lipmann, in "The Origins of Prebiological Systems" (S. Fox, ed.), p. 259. Academic Press, New York, 1965.
4. R. L. Lindeman, *Ecology* 23, 399 (1942).
5. D. M. Gates, "Energy Exchange in the Biosphere." Harper, New York, 1962.
6. F. E. Round, "The Biology of the Algae." St. Martin's Press, New York, 1965.
7. R. A. Lewin (ed.), "Physiology and Biochemistry of Algae." Academic Press, New York, 1961.
8. H. J. Morowitz, *Biochim. Biophys. Acta* 40, 340 (1960).
9. R. B. Roberts, P. H. Abelson, D. B. Cowie, E. T. Bolton, and R. J. Britten, "Studies of Biosynthesis in *E. Coli*." Publ. 607, Carnegie Inst. of Washington, Washington, D.C., 1955.
10. Selected values of chemical thermodynamic properties. *Circ. 500, Natl. Bur. Std.*, Washington, D.C., 1952.
11. G. S. Parks and H. M. Huffman, "The Free Energies of Some Organic Compounds." Chem. Catalog Co., New York, 1932.
12. W. M. Latimer, "Oxidation Potentials." Prentice-Hall, Englewood Cliffs, New Jersey, 1952.
13. E. S. Domalski and I. Halow, *Natl. Bur. Std. (U.S.) Rept.* 8641 (1965).
14. Calculated from the bond energies for the imidazole ring and the heat of formation of alanine.
15. E. S. Domalski and I. Halow, *Natl. Bur. Std. (U.S.) Rept.* 8906 (1965).
16. Calculated from the ribose value using correction factors in Ref. (*11*), p. 210.
17. Mean purine value from thymine and uracil.
18. Calculated from thymine value using corrections factors from Ref. (*11*), p. 210.
19. Calculated from data given in N. Adriaanse, H. Dekker, and J. Coops, *Rec. Trav. Chim.* 84, 393 (1965).
20. E. P. Egan, Jr. and Z. T. Wakefield, *J. Phys. Chem.* 61, 1500 (1937).
21. J. O. Hutchens, A. G. Cole, and J. W. Stout, *J. Am. Chem. Soc.* 82, 4813 (1960).
22. H. M. Huffman and E. L. Ellis, *J. Am. Chem. Soc.* 59, 2150 (1937).
23. J. O. Hutchens, A. G. Cole, R. A. Robie, and J. W. Stout, *J. Biol. Chem.* 238, 2407 (1963).

24. H. M. Huffman and E. L. Ellis, *J. Am. Chem. Soc.* **57**, 46 (1935).
25. Estimated from other amino acid values.
26. J. O. Hutchens, A. G. Cole, and J. W. Stout, *J. Phys. Chem.* **67**, 1128 (1963).
27. J. O. Hutchens, A. G. Cole, and J. W. Stout, *J. Biol. Chem.* **239**, 591 (1964).
28. A. G. Cole, J. O. Hutchens, and J. W. Stout, *J. Phys. Chem.* **67**, 1852 (1963).
29. J. O. Hutchens, A. G. Cole, and J. W. Stout, *J. Biol. Chem.* **239**, 4194 (1964).
30. Estimated from glucose value assuming that the specific heat per gram is the same for the pentoses as for the hexoses.
31. Estimated from adenine and guanine values.
32. R. B. Stiehler and H. M. Huffman, *J. Am. Chem. Soc.* **57**, 1741 (1935).
33. J. E. Ahlberg, E. R. Blanchard, and W. O. Lundberg, *J. Chem. Phys.* **5**, 539 (1937).
34. Calculated from heat capacity data of W. S. Singleton, T. L. Ward, and F. G. Dolleas, *J. Am. Oil Chemists Soc.* **27**, 143 (1950).
35. C. A. Zittle and C. L. A. Schmidt, *J. Biol. Chem.* **108**, 161 (1935).
36. J. P. Greenstein and M. Winitz, "Chemistry of the Amino Acids." Wiley, New York, 1961.
37. J. B. Taylor and J. S. Rowlinson, *Trans. Faraday Soc.* **51**, 1183 (1955).
38. Work of Kolozovski as discussed in J. W. Lavrie, "Glycerol and the Glycols." Chem. Catalog Co., New York, 1928.
39. Calculated from data in Refs. (*12*) and (*20*).
40. Calculated from Ref. (*38*) and data of K. Beviton and H. A. Krebs, *Biochem. J.* **54**, 86 (1953).
41. Calculated from solubility data in "Handbook of Chemistry and Physics," 39th ed. Chem. Rubber Publ. Co., Cleveland, Ohio, 1958, and molar volume data in E. J. Cohn and J. T. Edsall, "Proteins, Amino Acids and Peptides." Reinhold, New York, 1943.
42. T. L. McMeekin, E. J. Cohn, and J. H. Weare, *J. Am. Chem. Soc.* **56**, 2173 (1936).
43. "Properties of the Nucleic Acid Derivatives" (Cal. Biochem., Los Angeles, California, 1964).
44. A. W. Ralston and C. W. Hoerr, *J. Org. Chem.* **7**, 546 (1942).
45. Calculated from Ref. (*36*) and data of K. Burton and H. A. Krebs, *Biochem. J.* **54**, 86 (1953).
46. R. D. Stiehler and H. M. Huffman, *J. Am. Chem. Soc.* **57**, 1741 (1935).
47. D. E. Green, *Biochem. J.* **28**, 1550 (1934).
48. S. Davis and A. D. McLaren, *J. Polymer Sci.* **3**, 16 (1948).
49. D. D. Eley and R. B. Leslie, *Advan. Chem. Phys.* **7**, 238 (1964).
50. F. Gorski, "Plant Growth and Entropy Production." Zaklad Fizjologii Roslin Pan, Krakow, Poland, 1966.
51. J. M. Sturtevant, *in* "Experimental Thermochemistry" (H. A. Skinner, ed.) Vol. II, Chap. 19. Wiley (Interscience), New York, 1962.
52. O. Meyerhof and H. Green, *J. Biol. Chem.* **178**, 655 (1949).
53. O. Meyerhof and P. Oesper, *J. Biol. Chem.* **179**, 1371 (1949).
54. H. A. Krebs and H. L. Kornberg, "Energy Transformations in Living Matter." Springer, Berlin, 1957.
55. D. Scott, *Ecology* **46**, 673 (1965).

V

Ecology

And God said: "Behold, I have given you every herb yielding seed, which is upon the face of all the earth, and every tree, in which is the fruit of a tree yielding seed,—to you it shall be for food; and to every beast of the earth, and to every fowl of the air, and to every thing that creepeth upon the earth, wherein there is a living soul, I have given every green herb for food." And it was so.

Genesis

In Chapter IV we reviewed the data and established computational mechanisms which allow us to deal with the concept of free energy of formation of living material relative to some standard state of the starting material. In this chapter it is our purpose to apply this concept to certain problems in cell division, predator–prey relations, and trophic ecology. Our aim is to combine the insights of thermodynamics with those of biochemistry and trophic ecology in order to examine the relationships between energy flows and biological processes. In addition, we will examine the organizational properties of energy flow in ecology and compare them with the concepts regarding energy flow in prebiological evolution which we discussed in Chapters II and III. We may thus begin to glimpse the transition from the prebiological to the biological.

In order to proceed as outlined, we must first examine certain aspects of biochemistry which will underlie our discussion. This examination is based in large part on the monograph of Krebs and Kornberg (1) which reviews in detail the energy transformation in living matter.

The first principle that we are concerned with is the ubiquity of energy mechanisms in biology. There is a general scheme, parts of which are common to all organisms, which is followed in the combustion of foodstuffs to produce energy that is utilizable in biological processes. In the overwhelming majority of cases, the energy produced in the breakdown of biomass is stored as chemical energy in the pyrophosphate bonds of adenosine triphosphate (ATP). In the words of Krebs and Kornberg, "The first major stage, then, of the energy transformations in living matter culminates in the synthesis of pyrophosphate bonds of ATP, at the expense of the free energy of the degradation of foodstuffs. The overall thermodynamic efficiency of this process is estimated at 60–70%. This is high when compared with the efficiency of man-made machines depending on the burning of a fuel as a source of energy. The greater efficiency is possible because living matter is not a heat engine, but a 'chemical' engine organized in a special manner."

The transformation of the potential chemical energy of biomass to a utilizable form occurs in three phases, as outlined in Table 5-1. In the first phase, digestive enzymes hydrolyze the macromolecules down to their monomeric constituents. In the second phase, the released monomers are partially oxidized to one of three substances; acetic acid in the form of acetyl coenzyme A, α-ketoglutarate, and oxaloacetate. These three compounds all participate in the tricarboxylic acid cycle and so funnel into a common reaction pathway. In a complete cycle the material is further oxidized to two carbon dioxide molecules and four pairs of

TABLE 5-1

The Three Main Phases of Energy Production from Foodstuffs [a]

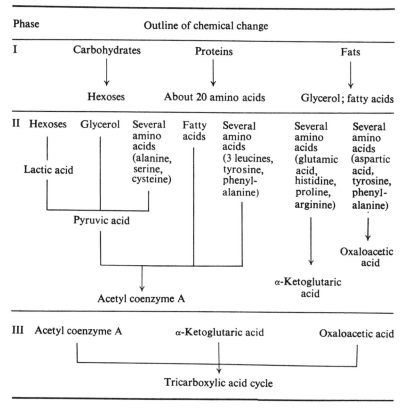

Phase	Outline of chemical change		
I	Carbohydrates	Proteins	Fats
	↓	↓	↓
	Hexoses	About 20 amino acids	Glycerol; fatty acids

II Hexoses Glycerol Several amino acids (alanine, serine, cysteine) Fatty acids Several amino acids (3 leucines, tyrosine, phenylalanine) Several amino acids (glutamic acid, histidine, proline, arginine) Several amino acids (aspartic acid, tyrosine, phenylalanine)

Lactic acid → Pyruvic acid → Acetyl coenzyme A

α-Ketoglutaric acid

Oxaloacetic acid

III Acetyl coenzyme A   α-Ketoglutaric acid   Oxaloacetic acid

Tricarboxylic acid cycle

[a] From Krebs (2).

hydrogen atoms, which are subsequently oxidized by O_2 with a concomitant release of energy. This last process of oxidative phosphorylation leads to the production of ATP. The steps of the tricarboxylic acid cycle are shown in Fig. 5-1.

The universality of the schemes of Table 5-1 and Fig. 5-1 underlies trophic dynamics. It is the common denominator of food chains. The primary requirement of a predator is that it can extract energy from its prey. The existence of a trophic network requires that common energy-yielding molecules connect all points in the network through which energy must flow. The existence of a small and ubiquitous set of energy-yielding reactions, as well as the ubiquity of macromolecular constituents, guarantees the possibility of this kind of interrelatedness. If this were not so, there could be a series of non biochemically-interacting ecological systems inhabiting the same niches. This is, of course, contrary to experience and imposes a good deal of biochemical overlap as a *sine qua non* of food chains and other aspects of trophic ecology.

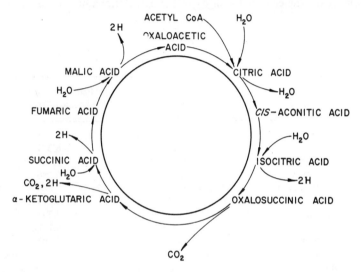

FIG. 5-1. The tricarboxylic acid cycle. One of the ubiquitous systems for energy conversion in living systems.

A number of other energy-yielding reactions are possible for special fermentations, but they all are related to Table 5-1 through the utilization of lactate or pyruvate. In many organisms the pentose-phosphate cycle represents an alternative energy-yielding pathway for glucose. It seems likely that there are other energy pathways yet to be discovered, but it also seems most probable that they will closely relate to present pathways and will not alter our concepts of the major energy-yielding pathways.

We now turn to the question of the actual energy levels of living systems. In Chapter IV we calculated that our theoretical biomass plus O_2 was 5.231 kcal/gm higher and 0.421 entropy units lower than the starting materials. If we look at the reverse of the synthesis in case I on page 81, we note that it corresponds to the usual bomb calorimeter oxidation of biomass to CO_2, H_2O, and N_2. Heats of combustion of biological materials should then provide a check of the validity of the enthalpy calculated in Chapter IV. Since dry material is burned in the calorimeter, we need to correct the data to the dry state, giving 5.240 kcal/gm as the calculated heat of combustion of biomass.

Experimental data are available on a number of plant and animal systems and some are presented in Tables 5-2 and 5-3. The data provide support for the essential validity of the calculations just outlined.

TABLE 5-2

HEATS OF COMBUSTION OF ANIMAL MATERIAL[a]

Organism	Species	Heat of combustion (kcal/ash-free gm)
Ciliate	*Tetrahymena pyriformis*	−5.938
Hydra	*Hydra littoralis*	−6.034
Green hydra	*Chlorohydra viridissima*	−5.729
Flatworm	*Dugesia tigrina*	−6.286
Terrestrial flatworm	*Bipalium kewense*	−5.684
Aquatic snail	*Succinea ovalis*	−5.415
Brachiopod	*Gottidia pyramidata*	−4.397
Brine shrimp	*Artemia* sp. (nauplii)	−6.737
Cladocera	*Leptodora kindtii*	−5.605
Copepod	*Calanus helgolandicus*	−5.400
Copepod	*Trigriopus californicus*	−5.515
Caddis fly	*Pycnopsyche lepido*	−5.687
Caddis fly	*Pycnopsyche guttifer*	−5.706
Spit bug	*Philenus leucopthalmus*	−6.962
Mite	*Tyroglyphus lintneri*	−5.808
Beetle	*Tenebrio molitor*	−6.314
Guppie	*Lebistes reticulatus*	−5.823

[a] From Slobodkin and Richman (3).

The range of values makes it clear that we need to reformulate the concept of biomass with a more detailed view which reflects the differences between different organisms. A study by Odum *et al.* (5) enables us to see clearly the dependence of heats of formation on the gross chemical composition. These investigators studied the heats of combustion in birds having widely different fat contents due to the stage in the migratory season in which they were taken; the results are shown in Table 5-4.

TABLE 5-3

ENERGY VALUES IN AN *Andropogon virginicus* OLD-FIELD
COMMUNITY IN GEORGIA[a]

Component	Energy value (kcal/ash-free gm)
Green grass	−4.373
Standing dead vegetation	−4.290
Litter	−4.139
Roots	−4.167
Green herbs	−4.288
Average	−4.251

[a] From Golley (4).

TABLE 5-4

HEATS OF COMBUSTION OF MIGRATORY AND NONMIGRATORY BIRDS[a]

Sample	Ash-free material (kcal/gm)	Fat ratio (% dry weight as fat)
Fall birds	−8.08	71.7
Spring birds	−7.04	44.1
Nonmigrants	−6.26	21.2
Extracted bird fat	−9.03	100.0
Fat extracted: fall birds	−5.47	0.0
spring birds	−5.41	0.0
nonmigrants	−5.44	0.0

[a] From Odum *et al.* (5).

Since the heats of formation depend, as would be expected, on the composition, a formal representation can be made in the following way:

$$\Delta H = \Delta H_{fat} f_{fat} + \Delta H_{protein} f_{protein}$$
$$+ \Delta H_{carbohydrate} f_{carbohydrate} \tag{5-1}$$

$$f_{fat} + f_{protein} + f_{carbohydrate} = 1 \tag{5-2}$$

where ΔH represents the individual enthalpies of formation and f is the fraction of the dry biomass of a particular kind. Similar linear equations can be written for the entropies of formation.

Heats of combustion of biological materials can be calculated from the data in Chapter IV and are, in many cases, available experimentally. Values are summarized by Watt and Merrill (6) for a large number of plant and animal materials; selected data are presented in Table 5-5.

TABLE 5-5

HEAT OF COMBUSTION OF COMPONENTS OF BIOMASS[a]

Material	ΔH protein (kcal/gm)	ΔH fat (kcal/gm)	ΔH carbohydrate (kcal/gm)
Eggs	−5.75	−9.50	−3.75
Gelatin	−5.27	−9.50	
Glycogen	—	—	−4.19
Meat, fish	−5.65	−9.50	—
Milk	−5.65	−9.25	−3.95
Fruits	−5.20	−9.30	−4.00
Grain	−5.80	−9.30	−4.20
Sucrose			−3.95
Glucose			−3.75
Mushroom	−5.00	−9.30	−4.10
Yeast	−5.00	−9.30	−4.20

[a] From Watt and Merrill (6).

From the data in Chapter IV we can calculate the heat of combustion of a model protein system. This yields 5.82 kcal/gm dry weight compared with the range of values 5.00–5.80 presented in Table 5-5. The heat of combustion of pure glucose is 3.74 kcal/gm which is a characteristic value for carbohydrates. A maximum heat of combustion for fats is calculated for glycerol tristearate and found to be 11.17 kcal/gm. If we consider one of the stearates replaced by a phosphate, the calculated value is 9.23 kcal/gm. The values, based on the chemistry of pure compounds, are thus in reasonable agreement with the combustion experiments on biological material. If we refer all of our data to N_2, CO_2, H_2O, H_2SO_4, and H_3PO_4 as the ground state, then the heats of combustion will be the same as the heats of formation. From an examination of Table 4-12 it is clear that for the overall process, the ΔH term (enthalpy) is the dominant one in ΔF (Gibbs free energy). For the present overall examination of trophic energy relations, we will consider ΔF as approximated by ΔH.* We will later return to a more detailed discussion of the entropy. Thus, Eqs. (5-1) and (5-2) establish a measure of energy of formation as a function of over-all composition. From the data presented we can assume the following average values:

$$\Delta H_{\text{protein}} = -5.50 \text{ kcal/gm}$$

$$\Delta H_{\text{fat}} = -9.30 \text{ kcal/gm}$$

$$\Delta H_{\text{carbohydrate}} = -4.10 \text{ kcal/gm}$$

It can be seen from Tables 5-3 to 5-5 that the primary producers have a lower free energy of formation than the upper trophic levels. Therefore, there are strong energy constraints in moving material up the trophic pyramid and, of necessity, much of the material in the primary trophic level must be degraded to raise the rest of the material to an appropriate free energy level. Thus, there are strong energy constraints to trophic efficiencies.

It is useful to represent graphically the free energy as a function of composition of biomass. To do this, we construct a graph in which the abscissa is protein fraction (f_{protein}) and the ordinate is fat fraction (f_{fat}). Since the overall system is represented by Eq. (5-2), a point on this graph uniquely represents a possible composition. The free energy of formation is given by

$$\Delta F = -5.50 f_{\text{protein}} - 9.30 f_{\text{fat}} - 4.10(1 - f_{\text{protein}} - f_{\text{fat}}) \qquad (5\text{-}3)$$

Isoenergetic loci are straight lines in this representation; Fig. 5-2 is a graph of this type. The primary trophic level occupies a small energy triangle in the lower left-hand corner of the graph. Most animals have relatively low carbohydrate levels and lie on the graph in a zone along the zero carbohydrate line. This emphasizes the major jump in moving material from primary producers into animal biomass.

We are now in a position to examine trophic transformations from the point of view of thermodynamics and to see where the analysis in these terms limits or better defines the problem. Figure 5-3 is a flow chart representing the major processes in the transfer of biomass between trophic levels. We have specifically included microorganisms in our

* The procedure of approximating the Gibbs free energy by the enthalpy is, in general, a risky one and care must be taken not to permanently forget the $T \Delta S$ term. In much of the energetic literature of ecology, the heat of combustion is taken as the sole thermodynamic parameter necessary to characterize the system. Scott has discussed this problem (7) in an article containing many useful insights. He has also critically reviewed the use of combustion data.

scheme, since the digestive tract of almost all metazoa contains micro-organisms which play a significant role in the metabolism and energy transformations of the organism (*8*). Since the microorganisms live inside the host, it is easier to consider them in a general scheme than to

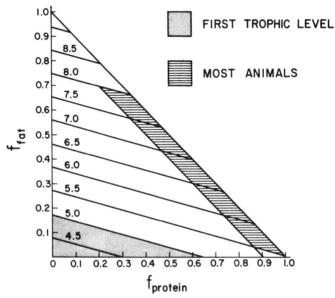

FIG. 5-2. Relation between macromolecular composition and heat of combustion for living organisms. First trophic level is represented in the lower left-hand corner of the graph. Most animal species are in the lined portion of the graph.

try to formulate two independent interacting energy budgets. Three rules govern each step in the flow diagram of Fig. 5-3.

(1) Mass is conserved. Specifically the number of atoms of each type is conserved.

(2) Energy is conserved.

(3) Entropy increases.

The ingestion step establishes the amount of matter and energy entering the system. The ingested material may either be parts of an organism from a lower trophic level or detritus. ("Detritus" is used here to mean nonliving products of living organisms.) The energy entering the system must either appear as heat, as work in the most general sense, or as chemical potential energy of biomass or products.

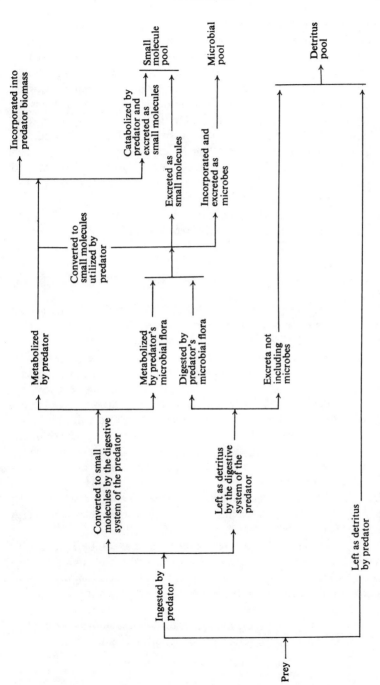

Fig. 5-3.   Flow chart showing the biomass conversions between predator, prey, microorganisms, and detritus.

In order to enter the metabolic processes of either the predator or the predator's microbes, the ingested material must first be split into relatively small molecules. This may be stated as a general rule of ecology: The utilization of prey biomass by a predator involves its degradation into its monomeric constituents. This is a key point of contact between biochemistry, ecology, and thermodynamics. There are two reasons for the degradation to monomers. First, the ubiquitous energy utilization mechanism already discussed employs small molecules. Second, the synthesis of macromolecules in living systems always proceeds through monomers. Since many macromolecules are information-specific and genetically determined, it is not possible to utilize them directly; they must be degraded to common components. This process involves a heat release of about 16.4 cal/gm and an entropy increase of 0.210 eu/gm, corresponding to a decrease in Gibbs free energy of 79 cal/gm. There are no processes by which to couple this free energy release to do useful work so that this portion of the ingested energy is lost to the predator, the enthalpy change eventually being transferred to heat in the environment.

One important exception to the breakdown and utilization rule should be noted. This is the phenomenon of genetic transformation by deoxyribonucleic acid (DNA). From experiments on bacterial transformation, it seems clear that large pieces of DNA are taken into the cell intact and whole cistrons or groups of cistrons are then incorporated into the cell's genome. This process generally requires close homology between the donor and receptor DNA. The total mass of material transferred in this way in natural habitats is probably negligibly small, so that while transformation may be of great genetic and evolutionary significance, it is a very minor pathway in trophic ecology.

The small molecules produced by the digestive enzymes of the predator or its bacteria now enter the usual pathways of intermediary metabolism where they are either degraded to yield energy and are subsequently excreted, or are incorporated into predator macromolecules. The energy produced is used for three basic processes.

1. Maintenance. As already noted, a nonequilibrium system isolated from energy sources slowly decays toward equilibrium. Although thermodynamics does not provide a time scale, such a system moves toward more disordered states, and a constant expenditure of work is required to restore the system to its proper state. Two examples will illustrate this point. In a living organism the macromolecules, such as proteins, are relatively unstable and are constantly undergoing thermal denaturation. In order to renature the proteins, they must be digested to amino acids and resynthesized. This process takes energy and, consequently, work must constantly be done to maintain the "static" molecular structure of a living organism. For a second example, suppose the functioning state of an organism requires a concentration difference of ions across a biological membrane. The concentration gradient is originally produced by the active transport of ions. In general, there will be a small leakage of ions back across the membrane from the high chemical potential side to the low. In order to maintain the state of the system, work must constantly be done to pump ions back to the high side. If the leak rate is u moles of ion per second and the chemical potentials are μ_H and μ_L on the high and low sides respectively, then the energy must be supplied at a rate exceeding $u(\mu_H - \mu_L)$ in order to maintain the system. Maintenance energy must thus be used to combat the spontaneous entropy production which characterizes nonequilibrium systems.

Any attempts to analyze maintenance energy from a physical point of view rest heavily on the physical and chemical details of the system being studied. One aspect, however, the thermal denaturation of macromolecules, appears to be susceptible to some generalizations. Among the quantitatively most plentiful macromolecules, proteins appear to be most sensitive to thermal effects. A denatured protein must be completely degraded to amino acids by the organism. This constant breakdown of proteins leads to substantial amino acid turnover in mammalian systems. According to White *et al.* (9), a 70-kg adult man synthesizes and degrades about 70 gm of protein nitrogen per day. Since the total nitrogen content of such an individual is about 900 gm, this indicates a protein turnover of about 7.7 % per day. All of this protein turnover does not result from protein denaturation; cell death and autolysis by proteolytic enzymes also contribute to the turnover. Part of the basal metabolism contributes energy to the resynthesis of this protein.

Since proteins are in one sense a fairly uniform set of molecules, all being polymers of the same twenty α-amino acids (with the exception of proline) linked by peptide bonds, one might anticipate that common features would exist in the thermal stability. Data on the thermal denaturation of proteins have been reviewed by Eyring and Stearn (*10*) and, subsequently, by Stearn (*11*). The kinetics of most protein inactivation is exponential and follows an equation of the form

$$N = N_0 \exp(-k_1 t) \tag{5-4}$$

where N is the amount of active or native protein, N_0 is the original amount of active material, t is time, and k_1 is a rate constant which may be expressed in terms of the activation enthalpy and entropy as discussed in Chapter I. Consequently, data on thermal inactivation are generally expressed in terms of $\Delta H^{\ddagger}$ and $\Delta S^{\ddagger}$ (Table 5-6).

TABLE 5-6

THERMAL INACTIVATION OF PROTEINS AND RELATED SYSTEMS IN AQUEOUS
SOLUTION

Substance	$\Delta H^{\ddagger}$	$\Delta S^{\ddagger}$	Substance	$\Delta H^{\ddagger}$	$\Delta S^{\ddagger}$
Insulin	35,600	23.8	Tetanolysin	172,650	459.0
Trypsin	40,200	44.7	Rennen	89,300	208.0
Catalase	50,500	81.0	Egg albumin, pH 7.7	134,300	317.1
Pepsin	55,600	113.3	pH 3.4	96,800	223.7
Peroxidase (milk)	185,300	466.0	pH 1.35	35,200	36.3
Enterokinase	42,160	52.8	Yeast invertase, pH 5.7	52,400	84.7
Trypsin kinase	44,260	57.6	pH 5.2	86,400	185.0
Proteinase (pancreatic)	37,860	40.6	pH 4.0	110,400	262.5
Amylase malt	41,600	52.3	pH 3.0	74,400	152.4
Emulsin	44,900	65.3	Inactivation of tobacco		
Leucosin	84,300	185.0	mosaic virus	40,000	18.0
Hemoglobin	75,600	152.7	Inactivation of T_1		
Hemolysin (goat)	198,000	537.0	bacteriophage	95,000	207.0
Vibriolysin	128,000	326.0	Average	82,000	164.1

We can average the values from known proteins and obtain a $\Delta H^{\ddagger}$ of 82,000 cal/mole and a $\Delta S^{\ddagger}$ of 164.1 cal/°C mole. Averaging the energy functions is equivalent to taking the geometric mean of the rate values. If we assume that this average holds as an appropriate average for the protein of biomass, we can calculate the necessary replacement rate as a function of temperature. The values are given in Table 5-7 and shown in Fig. 5-4. Organisms utilizing this class of proteins would have difficulty in homeostasis at temperatures much above the mid-forties because the recycling of protein would impose a heavy burden on the metabolic system. The exponential character of this type of curve makes it clear that there must be a sharp cutoff in the temperature at which organisms homeostat. Figure 5-4 contains a number of representative temperatures of animals which possess some temperature regulation. It appears from

TABLE 5-7

THERMAL DENATURATION OF AVERAGE PROTEIN (BIOMASS) AS A FUNCTION
OF TEMPERATURE

Temp. (°C)	Rate (sec⁻¹)	Amount replaced in 24 hr (%)	Temp. (°C)	Rate (sec⁻¹)	Amount replaced in 24 hr (%)
37	1.25×10^{-7}	1.08	44	2.37×10^{-6}	20.50
38	1.89×10^{-7}	1.63	45	3.52×10^{-6}	28.65
39	3.70×10^{-7}	3.20	46	5.35×10^{-6}	46.20
40	5.12×10^{-7}	4.42	47	7.92×10^{-6}	68.40
41	6.62×10^{-7}	5.71	48	1.35×10^{-5}	116.64
42	1.05×10^{-6}	9.08	49	1.81×10^{-5}	161.51
43	1.50×10^{-6}	13.81	50	2.71×10^{-5}	234.14

these data that animals do homeostat at temperatures lower than those at which they are menaced by the high rate of protein denaturation.

There are of course thermophilic organisms, in particular, a number

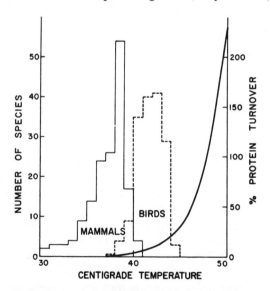

FIG. 5-4. Graph of temperature of homeostasis versus number of species that regulate at that temperature. Also shown are protein turnover rates as a function of temperature. Most species regulate at temperatures where the thermal decay of proteins is small.

of microbial species, which appear to grow at temperatures up to 65°C. These organisms replicate at a sufficiently rapid rate so that the 24-hour protein replacement load is not an appropriate parameter. Koffler (*12*) argues that thermophiles synthesize proteins which are inherently more heat stable than the usual class of mesophilic proteins. It is not easy to see what features in protein structure would confer this heat resistance. Such a class of proteins would lead to a curve in Fig. 5-4 which would be displaced to the right. The curve shape would, however, be the same and our reasoning would hold that large organisms must exist in a temperature range in which the protein replacement rate can be satisfied without burdening the energy production system.

   2. Synthesis. Since the breakdown of macromolecules to smaller structures releases energy, energy must be supplied in the reverse process. This is the irreducible minimum energy loss in the transfer of biomass between trophic levels. We can use our previously developed information to calculate what this loss must be. Assume for the moment that the chemical composition of predator and prey are the same and correspond to that of the biomass in Table 4-1. We then will require 79 cal/gm to synthesize macromolecules. This must come from the oxidation of some of the ingested material. From Tables 4-7 and 4-5 and using case III, we can calculate that the free energy change on oxidation to CO_2, H_2O, and NH_3 is 4530 cal/gm. As previously noted in this chapter, such energy can be converted to phosphate-bond energy with an average efficiency of about 65% so that the available energy is 2901 cal/gm. Thus, 0.023 gm of ingested material must be used to obtain the energy for synthesis of a gram of macromolecule. Actually, the coupling of phosphate-bond energy to synthesis is not 100% as would be indicated by this calculation.

   If we examine the actual synthetic pathways, we note that, in fact, two phosphate bonds are hydrolyzed in the synthesis of each macromolecular linkage. This point has been extensively discussed by Kornberg (*13*) and has recently been stated by Watson (*14*) as: "The general rule exists that $P\sim P$ is released in almost all biosynthetic reactions. Almost as soon as it is made, it is enzymatically broken down to $2P$, thereby making impossible a reversal of the biosynthetic reaction. The great utility of the $P\sim P$ split provides an explanation for why ATP, not ADP, is the primary energy donor. ADP cannot transfer a high-energy group and, at the same time, produce $P\sim P$ groups as a byproduct."

   The free energy change in going from adenosine triphosphate to adenosine monophosphate and two orthophosphates is 14 kcal/mole.

Since 1 gm of biomass involves 82.2×10^{-4} moles of polymeric linkages, 115 cal/gm are required. This necessitates the oxidation of 0.038 gm of biomass per gram of material synthesized. The macromolecular synthetic processes are remarkably efficient in utilizing energy for the transformation of biomass from one species to another.

In the previous paragraph we have assumed that the predator and its food had the same molecular composition. In general, they will not be exactly the same and energy will have to be expended in converting the small molecules into their appropriate forms. In general, the predator biomass may be at a higher free energy than the food and large quantities of nutrient must be oxidized to raise the energy of the associated incorporated material. Referring to Tables 5-2 and 5-3, we note that, in general, the first trophic level supplies food about 4 kcal/gm above ground level, where upper trophic levels are at an energy of about 5.5 kcal/gm or higher. Such a system can, at most, be 77 % efficient in transfer between trophic levels. A second restriction enters for such systems. The lowest trophic level is also low in nitrogen so that ingesting sufficient nitrogen for growth can limit the efficiency rather than energy limitations. If we turn to Table 3-2, we note that man is 5.14 % nitrogen while alfalfa is 0.825 % nitrogen. If we were to convert alfalfa biomass into human biomass at maximum efficiency, we would require (5.14/0.825) or 6.22 gm dry weight of alfalfa per gram dry weight of human biomass, which is an efficiency of conversion of 16 %. In the adult stage of animals, the problem of nitrogen balance changes and an animal must ingest excess nitrogen compounds in order to get sufficient maintenance energy. Since no method exists of storing nitrogen, various pathways of nitrogen excretion exist via such compounds as uric acid, urea, and amino acids. An examination of Fig. 5-2 shows the nitrogen gap expressed as protein difference between the primary trophic level and upper trophic levels. This factor greatly limits the maximum possible efficiency of total mass transfer.

3. *Mechanical Energy.* Most animals expend some energy in the mechanical motion associated with obtaining food, avoiding predators, locating suitable environments, and procreating. The processes are highly species-specific and will not, at the moment, be subject to any thermodynamic generalizations. It should be noted, however, that this category of energy cannot be sharply distinguished from maintenance energy. Moving into the warm sun to acquire heat is as much a part of the maintenance energy as obtaining the thermal energy by oxidation of carbohydrates.

The thermodynamic analysis that we have been discussing allows us to raise some questions of interest about the replication of cells. The problem we wish to focus attention on is the formation of two cells from one in an isothermal environment (15). This may be represented as

$$1 \text{ cell} + \text{nutrient} \rightarrow 2 \text{ cells} + \text{waste products} \qquad (5\text{-}5)$$

As the initial cell plays a catalytic role, we need not consider it in our balance equation and can rewrite the formal description as

$$\text{nutrient} \rightarrow \text{cell} + \text{waste products} \qquad (5\text{-}6)$$

This process is the same as the production of biomass from intermediates, which we have previously discussed, except that in the production of waste products, we have a linked process producing the energy to drive the synthesis. Of course, the case we are considering involves an organism growing in a complete medium with a total supply of the necessary building blocks for cell synthesis. Note that even under optimal conditions, thermodynamic factors require that the synthesis of new cellular material be accompanied by the production of waste products. This may be viewed as an ecological generalization which is derivable from a thermodynamic analysis of the process. From our previous consideration of the two-phosphate bond model of synthesis and the assumption that the ΔH for phosphate-bond hydrolysis is 5 kcal/mole, the overall process will be exothermic and will release 8 kcal/bond. An additional 8 kcal are converted to heat during the synthesis of the phosphate bonds. Thus, in the synthesis of new biomass, the organism will produce heat at the rate of 16 kcal/polymer bond or 132 cal/gm. This is a minimum figure based on the most efficient known processes and assuming no heat losses for maintenance energy.

Actual data are available on the heat production of growing bacteria, based on the calorimetric studies of Bayne-Jones and Rhees (16). Their data would indicate an actual heat of growth of about 2400 cal/gm, a figure about 20 times the thermodynamic minimum of 132 cal/gm. Their experiments were on *E. coli* growing in a medium of Difco peptone.

We now proceed to investigate one aspect of the heat production accompanying synthesis, that is, the necessary temperature rise during growth and cell replication. Consider a simplified model of a sphere which grows from a volume of v to $2v$ and then divides into two spheres. The average volume during this process is $\frac{3}{2}v$ and the average radius is $(9v/8\pi)^{1/3}$. If the cell density is ρ, the nonaqueous mass increase is $\rho v/4$.

If the division time is τ, the cells can be regarded as a uniform spherical heat source of source strength q equal to

$$q = \frac{(\rho v/4)\,\Delta H_m}{\frac{3}{2}v\tau}$$

$$= \frac{\rho\,\Delta H_m}{6\tau} \tag{5-7}$$

where ΔH_m is the heat produced per unit weight of biomass synthesized. For a sphere containing a uniform heat source q, we can use the theory of thermal conductivity to compute the difference between the center temperature and the surface temperature which may be taken to be that of the thermal reservoir.

$$T_{\text{center}} - T_{\text{surface}} = \frac{qr^2}{\kappa}$$

$$= \frac{\rho\,\Delta H_m r^2}{6\kappa\tau} \tag{5-8}$$

The thermal conductivity can be approximated by that of water ($\kappa = 0.0014$ cal/deg cm sec), while ρ, the density of biomass, is about 1.08 gm/cm^3. In a normal bacterial cell of 1 μ radius replicating in 20 minutes, ΔT for a maximally efficient conversion is the order of 5×10^{-7} degrees and is trivial. However, Eq. (5-8) does limit cell size and replication rate and provides a thermodynamic upper limit on the size of replicating systems without special heat exchange mechanisms. If we assume that $\Delta H_m = 2400$ cal/gm, then we can rewrite Eq. (5-8) as

$$\Delta T = 308{,}800\,\frac{r^2}{\tau} \tag{5-9}$$

where r is in centimeters and τ is in seconds. If we assume that the maximum tolerable temperature rise is 10°C, we can relate τ and r as in Table 5-8. In the usual range of biological synthesis, the heat release does not provide a significant limitation to the rate of production of new material. Diffusion, in general, turns out to be a stronger constraint on the size of systems not having circulatory systems (17).

Thus far in this part of Chapter V, as well as in Chapter IV, we have developed the thermodynamic formalism and have discussed some of the available data necessary to examine ecology in terms of energy flow. It should by now be clear that such a discipline is in its infancy and requires experimental programs to obtain the thermochemical data on

TABLE 5-8

RELATIONSHIP BETWEEN CELL SIZE r AND
MINIMUM DIVISION TIME

r (cm)	Minimum division time
10^{-3}	30.9 msec
10^{-2}	3.09 sec
10^{-1}	5.15 min
10^0	8.53 hr
10^1	35.3 days

compounds of biological interest. In addition, more imaginative methods of obtaining energy data in field situations are also going to be required.

At this point, our analysis of ecology as well as evolution appears to be missing a principle. To attempt to glimpse the principle, we shall review the general argument which is the main theme of this book.

(a)   The surface of the earth belongs to that class of physical systems which receives energy from a source and gives up energy to a sink. There is a constant and (on the appropriate time scale) almost steady flow of energy through the system.

(b)   This flow of energy is a necessary and, we believe, sufficient condition to lead to molecular organization of the system experiencing the energy flow.

(c)   This flow of energy led to the formation of living systems, and ecological process is the continued maintenance of order by the energy flow. Thus, the problem of the origin of life and the development of the global ecosystem merge into one and the same problem.

(d)   The flow of energy causes cyclic flow of matter. This cyclic flow is part of the organized behavior of systems undergoing energy flux. The converse is also true; the cyclic flow of matter such as is encountered in biology requires an energy flow in order to take place. The existence of cycles implies that feedback must be operative in the system. Therefore, the general notions of control theory and the general properties of servo networks must be characteristic of biological systems at the most fundamental level of operation.

The principle we appear to be missing is a guide as to which of all the possible systems will, in fact, arise and evolve in a given energy flow situation. It may turn out that there are no general principles in this area and that each case must be worked out in full kinetic detail. In ecology, similarly, we would like some principle to indicate the path of the development of a climax community. Certain features seem to be of prime importance in the evolution of steady state systems.

1. The Atomic Composition. Contrary to the usual situation in thermodynamics where the general laws are independent of the details of the substances involved, in the steady state situation, compositional details are all important. The presence or absence of phosphorus would totally and completely alter the character of the entire biosphere. In respect to trace quantities of material, steady state systems react entirely differently from equilibrium systems. In the latter, the final concentrations are virtually unperturbed by small quantities of material, since these small quantities have small effects on the total energies. In nonequilibrium situations, rates may become all important, and the presence of trace materials may have a catalytic effect on some pathways and completely alter the steady state concentrations. This feature is one of the reasons why nonequilibrium systems are so difficult to study.

2. The Temperature. The compounds which can exist in a given environment for any extended period of time are determined, in part, by the temperature. Above a certain temperature, any structures dependent on covalent bonding become impossible.

3. The Form of the Energy Input. The nature of the energy source in terms of its temperature, its spectral distribution, its intensity and its periodicity may be expected to profoundly influence the intermediate system.

At this juncture, it would appear that a more detailed study of the kinetics, photochemistry, and molecular physics of steady state systems undergoing energy flow will provide the best hope of understanding the origin of life and the transition to an ecological system.

References

1. H. A. Krebs and H. L. Kornberg, "Energy Transformations in Living Matter." Springer, Berlin, 1957.
2. H. A. Krebs, *Brit. Med. Bull.* **9**, 97 (1953).
3. L. B. Slobodkin and S. Richman, *Nature* **191**, 299 (1961).
4. F. Golley, *Ecology* **42**, 581 (1961).
5. E. P. Odum, S. G. Marshall, and T. G. Marples, *Ecology* **46**, 901 (1965).
6. B. K. Watt and A. L. Merrill, "Composition of Foods." U.S. Dept. Agriculture Handbook 8, Washington, D.C., 1963.
7. D. Scott, *Ecology* **46**, 673 (1965).

8. T. D. Brock, "Principles of Microbial Ecology." Prentice-Hall, Englewood Cliffs, New Jersey, 1966.
9. A. White, P. Handler, and E. L. Smith, "Principles of Biochemistry." McGraw-Hill, New York, 1964.
10. H. Eyring and A. E. Stearn, *Chem. Rev.* **24**, 253 (1939).
11. A. E. Stearn, *Advan. Enzymol.* **9**, 25 (1949).
12. H. Koffler, *Bacteriol. Rev.* **21**, 227 (1957).
13. A. Kornberg, *in* "Horizons in Biochemistry" (M. Kosha and B. Pullman, eds.). Academic Press, New York, 1962.
14. J. D. Watson, "Molecular Biology of the Gene." Benjamin, New York, 1965.
15. H. J. Morowitz, *Biochim. Biophys. Acta* **40**, 340 (1960).
16. S. Bayne-Jones and R. S. Rhees, *J. Bacteriol.* **17**, 123 (1939).
17. N. Rashevsky, "Mathematical Biophysics." Univ. of Chicago Press, Chicago, Illinois, 1948.

VI

Order Information and Entropy

Flower in the crannied wall,
I pluck you out of the crannies,
I hold you here, root and all, in my hand,
Little flower—but if I could understand
What you are, root and all, and all in all,
I should know what God and man is

Alfred Lord Tennyson

In the previous chapters we have noted that the concepts of energy, order, work, and information are all closely interrelated and we have used them in an interchangeable way in analyzing the development and properties of biological systems. In this chapter we will try to make some of these concepts more precise so that we may begin to see more exact relations between biology and thermal physics. We begin by examining the formal connections between information, entropy, and work. This topic has been discussed extensively and reviewed by Brillouin (1) and we will concern ourselves here with only certain aspects of the problem, from the point of view of energy flow theory. Brillouin's general conclusion, starting from an analysis of the theory of physical measurements, is that the acquisition of one bit of information necessitates an overall increase of entropy of $k \ln 2$ somewhere in the system. Using an argument related to Szilard's original discussion of this problem (2), we proceed to a study of this point.

Examine first a very simple model system consisting of two bulbs of equal volume connected by a stopcock (Fig. 6-1). The system is immersed in an infinite isothermal reservoir of temperature T and contains one molecule of a perfect gas. The stopcock is closed so that there are two chambers, one with a gas molecule and one empty. If an observer knew in which chamber the molecule was, he would have one bit of information, since this is the amount of information in resolving a binary choice. Moreover, if the observer knew in which chamber the molecule was, he could rig up the system to a piston and could, by the laws of ordinary thermodynamics, recover an amount of work equal to

$$\Delta W = \int_{V_0}^{2V_0} p \, dV$$
$$= \int_{V_0}^{2V_0} \frac{nRT}{V} \, dV$$
$$= kT \ln 2 \qquad (6\text{-}1)$$

If some concern exists about having a piston engine run by only one molecule, we could build a system of a large number of pairs of bulbs and connect all the occupied sides and all the unoccupied sides, converting the problem to a macroscopic one. This will simply introduce a scale factor which will drop out in the final step, leaving the value of the amount of work per molecule as $kT \ln 2$.

If the information about which bulb the molecule is in could be obtained without doing work, we would have a violation of the Kelvin–Planck statement of the second law of thermodynamics (3). "It is impossible to construct an engine that, operating in a cycle, will produce no effect other than the extraction of heat from a reservoir and the performance of an equivalent amount of work." We must therefore conclude that the obtaining of one bit of information requires either the expenditure of $kT \ln 2$ units of work or, alternatively, the increase of $k \ln 2$ units of entropy somewhere in the system.

Work is required to get information. This is true in the limiting microworld as well as in macroscopic experience. The relationship of information to the second law might be generalized. All equilibrium systems contain $\frac{3}{2}nkT$ units of kinetic energy. Any information about the detailed

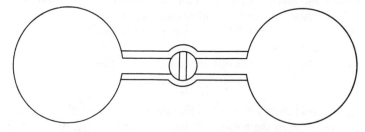

Fig. 6-1. Two bulbs connected by a stopcock, one containing a gas molecule and the second one empty.

microstate makes some of this energy available for external work. Therefore, in a very general sense, the Kelvin–Planck statement of the second law involves an energetic or entropic price on information about microstates. From the point of view of molecular theory our reasoning has been backwards; we started out with a gross macroscopic principle and derived results about gaining information about microstates. Brillouin developed a different approach. He analyzed physical measurement and showed that the obtaining of one bit of information involved the transfer of at least $kT \ln 2$ of energy from a source to a sink. This then constitutes a foundation for the second law, based on the theory of measurement in the microscopic realm. This is an extremely interesting development in that it allows us to get some additional insight into the second law from a microscopic or molecular point of view.

The relationship between energy and information that we have been discussing is very deeply rooted in thermodynamics and is intimately involved in the structure of the entire subject. In order to gain some insight into the application of thermodynamics to biology, it is necessary to examine this relation more closely. A further aspect of this subject, and a fitting place to start, is the relation of order and information to negative entropy which has been introduced into biology by Schrödinger (4) and others.

Information in the communication-theory sense begins with a set of messages, each with a probability p_i. In a long sequence of such messages the average information content per message is

$$I = -\sum p_i \ln_2 p_i \qquad (6\text{-}2)$$

This measure can be shown to have the necessary analytical properties and correspondence with our intuitive notions of information.

In statistical mechanics we start out with a system that can be in any of a large number of states i, each characterized by an energy ϵ_i. We then assert that in an ensemble of such systems, the probability of any system being in the ith state is p_i. We proceed to show that the equilibrium state of the ensemble is the one which maximizes the quantity

$$S = -k \sum p_i \ln p_i \qquad (6\text{-}3)$$

Equations (6-2) and (6-3) are functionally similar and point to a correspondence between the notions of entropy and information. Indeed, if we regard the knowledge of which microstate a system is in as equivalent to a message, then the average information in knowing the microstate of a given ensemble member would be

$$I_S = -\sum p_i \ln_2 p_i$$

$$= -\frac{1}{0.6932} \sum p_i \ln p_i \qquad (6\text{-}4)$$

so that

$$S = 0.6932kI \qquad (6\text{-}5)$$

The entropy is thus directly proportional to the information we would have if we knew which microstate the system was in. When we assert that the equilibrium state is the state of maximum entropy we therefore assert that it is the condition in which we are maximally ignorant of the microstate of the system. But this viewpoint involves a curious twist. In classical thermodynamics we assert that entropy is a property of the system (indeed, we go to great lengths to establish that it is a state function), whereas in the present analysis we are asserting that entropy is a measure of our ignorance of the exact microstate that a system is in. Brillouin (1) has commented on this point by noting that, "Entropy is usually described as measuring the amount of disorder in a physical system. A more precise statement is that entropy measures lack of information about the actual structure of the system. This lack of information introduces the possibility of a great variety of microscopically distinct structures, which we are, in practice, unable to distinguish from one another." We may then raise the point: is entropy a property of the system or of the observer or the relationship between them?

Some other simple examples may also illustrate this problem. Consider two chambers of equal volume immersed in an isothermal reservoir.

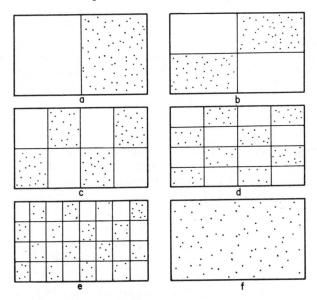

Fig. 6-2. Series of full and empty chambers. The full chambers contain a perfect gas. As we increase the number of chambers a–e, the configuration begins to approach the random distribution f.

If one chamber contains a mole of perfect gas and the second is empty (Fig. 6-2), then opening a valve between the two chambers causes an entropy increase of

$$\Delta S = R \ln\left(\frac{V_2}{V_1}\right) = R \ln 2 \qquad (6\text{-}6)$$

Since the internal energy of a perfect gas is a function of T only, we have

$$\Delta U = 0 = T \Delta S - \Delta W \qquad (6\text{-}7)$$

A reversible expansion can then lead to an amount of work

$$\Delta W = RT \ln 2 \tag{6-8}$$

Next, consider a four-chamber arrangement as shown in Fig. 6-2b. The entropy change and available work are still given by Eqs. (6-6) and (6-8). To carry the argument still further, we may go to an eight-chamber arrangement with four full and four empty chambers, or a sixteen-chamber arrangement with eight full and eight empty. In each case the final volume is twice the original volume and Eqs. (6-6) and (6-8) describe the changes in entropy and the maximum available work. If we carry this argument to microscopic dimensions, we will have a distribution of gas hardly different from the random distribution that would obtain if we allow the gas to uniformly fill the entire volume, but still able to yield a ΔW of $RT \ln 2$. Since entropy is supposedly a state function, we have a seeming paradox of two systems in the same state with different entropy measures, depending on how the systems arrived at their final states.

The answer is not difficult to find. In the first case we assumed that the available work is $RT \ln 2$. This ignored the fact that in order to hook up the system to a piston to produce work, it is necessary to know which chamber is full and which is empty. This is a binary decision which we have shown requires $kT \ln 2$ work units. The net available work is therefore $RT \ln 2 - kT \ln 2$. Since the ratio of R to k is Avogadro's number, which is very large, the small correction factor imposed by informational considerations need not concern us in macroscopic thermodynamics.

Let us further consider the problem posed in Fig. 6-2. Assume that we subdivided the large chamber so that there are N pairs of small chambers, where N is Avogadro's number. Consider two experimenters, the first who set up the system and knows which boxes are full and which are empty, and a second who approaches the system with no previous knowledge of its state. The first experimenter can get an amount of work $RT \ln 2$ out of the system while the second can get an amount of work $RT \ln 2 - NkT \ln 2 = 0$ out of the system. Using Eq. (6-7), the entropy changes of releasing the constraints are then

$$\text{First experimenter:} \quad \Delta S = R \ln 2$$
$$\text{Second experimenter:} \quad \Delta S = 0 \tag{6-9}$$

Thus, the same initial and final states, as already noted, lead to different entropy changes for the two observers. The entropy must then somehow involve the observer as well as the system being observed. The observer thus intrudes into the theory of statistical mechanics in as brash a way as he previously ventured into quantum theory and relativity. Note that the problem we have been discussing becomes important in the micro-domain and does not appreciably alter our view of macroscopic thermodynamics.

We now turn to a case of more macroscopic interest, which is suggested in Morrison's article (5) on the thermodynamics of self-reproduction. Consider the case of two chambers, each of volume V, immersed in an isothermal reservoir of temperature T and each containing a mole of a different perfect gas. If we allow the two to mix, classical thermodynamics predicts an entropy change of

$$\Delta S = -R(\ln \tfrac{1}{2} + \ln \tfrac{1}{2})$$

$$= 2R \ln 2 \qquad (6\text{-}10)$$

The question has been raised by Gibbs as to how different the two species of molecules need to be in order to have an entropy of mixing. For example, suppose in one chamber we had 2-deuteropentane, while in the other chamber we had 3-deuteropentane (Fig. 6-3); would we

$$
\begin{array}{ccccc}
\text{H} & \text{D} & \text{H} & \text{H} & \text{H} \\
| & | & | & | & | \\
\text{H--C--C--C--C--C--H} \\
| & | & | & | & | \\
\text{H} & \text{H} & \text{H} & \text{H} & \text{H}
\end{array}
$$

$$
\begin{array}{ccccc}
\text{H} & \text{H} & \text{D} & \text{H} & \text{H} \\
| & | & | & | & | \\
\text{H--C--C--C--C--C--H} \\
| & | & | & | & | \\
\text{H} & \text{H} & \text{H} & \text{H} & \text{H}
\end{array}
$$

Fig. 6-3.   2-Deuteropentane and 3-deuteropentane, species for which it would be extremely difficult to measure the entropy of mixing.

then measure an entropy of mixing? The Gibbs paradox has been answered in the following way: if we have passive membranes that can distinguish the two species, allowing one to pass and impermeable to the second, then we get an amount of pV work equal to $2RT \ln 2$. If we can obtain the pV work, there is a mixing entropy; if we cannot, there is either no entropy of mixing or an undetected entropy of mixing. Morrison has stated the problem as (5), "The ability to distinguish the marker position has yielded free energy, but only if semipermeable membranes capable of discriminating all the participant molecules are employed. An experimenter not sufficiently discriminating would be unable to detect the free energy potentially available; it would be made up fully by the undetected mixing entropy of a mixture he was unable to separate. But it cannot be held that this free energy contribution is not real; it is a source of work which is available only to changes carried on under appropriate constraints, but indeed so is every transfer of energy into work." Thus, we see that even in a macroscopic case, the entropy change is not entirely related to the system but depends on the knowledge and skill of the observer.

Our current concepts of thermodynamics are rooted in the industrial revolution and the attempts to determine how much mechanical work is available from heat engines. Entropy provides a measure of the work that is unavailable because of our lack of knowledge of the detailed state of the system. The whole structure acquires consistency only because it requires work to obtain information. If this were not true, a Maxwellian demon could indeed continuously violate the second law of thermodynamics. The second law and the entropy measure tell us as much about the observer as about the system. This accounts partially for the difficulty of the entropy concept. In steam-engine thermodynamics we do not require very detailed knowledge of the state of the system; however, in biology the case is entirely different as the phenomena depend on molecular detail. A misplaced methyl group can eventually kill a whale. The relationship between the observer and the system may thus achieve considerably more importance in biological thermodynamics than in previous considerations of a more coarse-grained type.

This introduces a very subtle point, since in biology we have the possibility that the observer and the system will, in fact, be the same. Since many of the epistemological problems of physics arise out of the nature of the interaction of the observer and the system, these will all have to be carefully reexamined for the case where the observer and system are one and the same. In considering this point we might look for the resolution of certain limitations in biological theory suggested by Bohr (6, 7) and more recently discussed in detail by Elsasser (8). In order to see this point fully, we will quote at considerable length from Elsasser's book "Atom and Organism."

"If we try to predict with precision the future behavior of an organism we must, according to physics, know the initial values of the positions and velocities of its constituent particles with sufficient accuracy. It might not be necessary to measure all of these at exactly the same moment, but they ought to be measured during some limited initial interval. If we cannot collect this precise information, prediction of the future behavior of the system becomes correspondingly limited. Now even in a relatively simple organism, a cell say, there are billions of orbital electrons which maintain a most intricate system of chemical bonds. The vital activity of the cell, especially metabolism, consists exactly in the changing of bonds, in the transfer processes which these bonding electrons undergo as time goes on. But quantum mechanics tells us that in order to localize an electron to within a reasonable accuracy on the molecular scale, say to within one angstrom, a physical interaction of the electron with the measuring probe (e.g., X-rays) must take place which, in the average, transmits a certain amount of interaction energy to the electron. Very simple calculations show that the average energy per measuring process is by no means negligible compared to the average bonding energy. Thus if we admit multiple measuring processes even as an idealization, a corresponding number of bonds will be dislocated or broken. In order to make valid predictions for an appreciable time ahead it would be necessary, in a system as complex dynamically and as interrelated as an organism, to determine quantitatively many if not most of the existing bonds. The energy conferred upon the tissue by virtue of the measurements becomes then so large that vast changes must take place: the system will be radically altered and disrupted and is no longer even approximately equal to the system which was at hand before the measurements were undertaken."

The previous discussion deals with the difficulty that an observer has in determining the microstate of a living organism without altering that microstate beyond all possible recognition. However, the problem of a system knowing its own microstate is vastly different from an outside observer knowing its microstate. That is, the system is the microstate and by virtue of being the microstate, has a great deal more knowledge of the microstate than is ever possible for an outside observer. Lest this seems like a word game, let us consider an example. When an enzyme and substrate form an intermediate complex, the enzyme does not have to perform a series of observations on the substrate molecule to see if it is sterically proper. By virtue of the enzyme being its own microstate and the substrate being its own microstate, they specifically interact without any necessity of an informational step. The argument between the reductionists and the nonreductionists may therefore hinge on the fact that a system can know its own microstate far better than is possible for an outside observer. This fact is implicitly used in the design of experiments for molecular biology. We do not, as implied by the Bohr–Elsasser argument, set up experiments to measure the position and momentum of all atoms in a living system; we rather use a different strategy of allowing the experimental living system to generate answers to questions that we pose by the experimental setup. This is the essence of what Platt (9) has called the strong inference method. In molecular biology we characteristically perform an operation on a group of cells. The cells, utilizing their own microstates, convert the experimental perturbation into some experimentally measurable parameter. We utilize these results in a strong inference framework to gain some information about the microstates of the cell, but it is almost always an indirect measurement that does not involve a measuring probe interacting with a cell.

The Bohr–Elsasser approach tends to overestimate the amount of measurement necessary to determine the microstate of a living cell and also tends to overestimate the amount of molecular specification necessary for a cell to function. First, note that a living cell is a system far from equilibrium and, as we shall subsequently show in detail, such systems yield far more information about the microstate from macroscopic measurements than do equilibrium systems. Determining the location in phase space of a nonequilibrium system therefore requires far fewer measurements than is true at equilibrium. Second, we have already noted in Chapter III in our discussion of the results of taking cells to very low temperatures, that measurement of velocities is not a necessary part of the informational description of the system, which immediately reduces by a factor of two the number of necessary measurements. Third, we do not know how precisely a microstate must be defined in order to predict future behavior. Some vague estimates of the required maximum precision of cell specification may be obtained from a study of how much random damage must be done in order to block some statistically predictable property such as cell division. A good deal of information is available on this subject from a study of the effects of ionizing radiation on cell replication.

Consider a typical radiation experiment on cells, the inactivation of *Mycoplasma gallisepticum* A 5969 by cobalt-60 gamma rays (10). The requisite dose for a 37% (1/e) survival is 20,300 roentgens, and the final inactivation curve is exponential. Since 1 roentgen in tissue corresponds to about 6×10^{11} primary ionizations (11) or 1.8×10^{12} total ionizations, the number of such ionizations per cell at the 37% dose is $20,300 \times 1.8 \times 10^{12} \times 10^{-13}$, where 10^{-13} cm^3 is the approximate volume of the cell.

As a rough approximation we assume that each ionization leads to one bond rupture so that the surviving cells each have about 3600 broken or rearranged bonds. It is thus possible to have considerable random damage and still have a functional, viable cell. This argument can be extended as noted in Table 6-1.

TABLE 6-1

SURVIVING FRACTION OF IRRADIATED *Mycoplasma* AS A
FUNCTION OF COVALENT BOND BREAKAGE

% Survival	Number of broken bonds
37	3600
1	16,400
0.1	24,400
0.0045	36,000

In order to round off our discussion of the relationship of entropy to the observer, we proceed to an argument pointed out by Gell-Mann (12) that the entropy considered just from the point of view of the system is an invariant, even for processes which are macroscopically irreversible. We will restrict our considerations to classical statistical mechanics and consider an ensemble of systems with the same volume, total energy, and number of particles which is describable by a distribution function in Γ space (a highly multidimensional space whose coordinates are the positions and momenta of all the particles of the system). At time $t = 0$, the density in phase space is $\rho(p_i, q_i, 0)$. Consider the distribution as a nonequilibrium one, arbitrarily far from equilibrium. If we allow the ensemble to age for a long time it will approach the equilibrium condition of the microcanonical ensemble. At equilibrium we can measure entropy as

$$S = \int_V \rho \ln \rho \, dV \qquad (6\text{-}11)$$

Let us consider the function $\int_V \rho \ln \rho \, dV$ as the ensemble proceeds from the initial nonequilibrium state to the final equilibrium ensemble. For the system we have been considering, the Liouville theorem holds and we note that

$$\frac{d\rho}{dt} = 0 \qquad (6\text{-}12)$$

The usual interpretation of this formula is that as any group of phase points moves through phase space, they must occupy a fixed volume dV.

Thus, any function of the form $\int_V f(\rho) \, dV$ where f is a function of ρ only, must remain time invariant, and S considered just from the point of view of the system must remain invariant in spite of any arbitrarily irreversible processes being described by the system.* If $\int_V \rho \ln \rho \, dV$ remains invariant we must again raise the question of what thermodynamic parameter changes in an irreversible process. Again, consider the case of two vessels, one with a mole of perfect gas and the other a vacuum. The initial state can be represented by an ensemble for which the Liouville theorem holds and, hence, the integral of $\rho \ln \rho \, dV$ must remain invariant during the diffusion of molecules into the empty chamber. (Assume that the two-chamber system is surrounded by an adiabatic envelope.) What changes in this case is our knowledge of positional coordinates of particles and, hence, our knowledge of which microstate the system is in. Having lost knowledge of the microstate implies loss of ability to extract work from the system, as has been noted in our previous comments on work and information.

Any nonequilibrium state provides more knowledge of the microstates from the macroscopic parameters than the corresponding equilibrium state into which it decays. This may be taken as proven by Jaynes' demonstration (13) that we may derive the equilibrium condition in statistical thermodynamics by seeking that condition in which the macroscopic constraints leave us maximally ignorant of the microscopic states.

A corollary of our being so much more ignorant of equilibrium systems is that they have the property of yielding zero averages for most macroscopic variables. Thus, in Callen's formulation of thermodynamics (14), he notes that, "There exist particular states (called equilibrium states) of simple systems that, macroscopically, are characterized completely by the internal energy U, the volume V, and the mole numbers N_1, N_2, ... N_r of the chemical components." The equilibrium states thus leave us with very few properties to measure and, consequently, reveal little of the microstate. This can be seen in terms of the Liouville theorem where the equilibrium ensemble is shown to have the property that ρ is a function of the energy alone. Since any momentum p_i occurs in the energy only as the square, values of p and $-p$ will occur with equal frequency so that any transport property will have a zero average at equilibrium. Again, equilibrium systems exhibit few macroscopic observables.

* All averages will not be time independent as ρ changes. For instance, any average of the form $\bar{\theta} = \int \theta(p, q)\rho(p, q, t) \, dV$ will, in general, be an explicit function of time.

What meaning can we then ascribe to order in terms of the previous analysis? Is it meaningful to inquire into the order of an equilibrium system? It would appear that since we are maximally ignorant of the microstate of an equilibrium system from our anthropomorphic (or observer's) point of view, the system must be one of maximum disorder. We may then consider an equilibrium system to be one in which our measure of order should have a zero value. Note should be taken here that we refer now to real equilibria that would obtain in systems aged for a long time, not the usual metastable equilibria. For simplicity in the following discussion, let us assume that unless otherwise stated, we are considering systems in contact with an isothermal reservoir so that our ensemble representation will be canonical.

Consider a nonequilibrium system placed in contact with an isothermal reservoir. Such a system will decay toward equilibrium and maximum disorder. Processes taking place in the system can only operate so as to decrease our knowledge of which microstate the system is in. Consequently, the entropy must increase. If the system is not at equilibrium, the usual formulation of thermodynamics states that $dS \geqslant 0$, but, in fact, if we consider long times or ensemble averages we must note that $dS > 0$. Every system in contact with a reservoir will move toward equilibrium given sufficient time. We introduce time in our thermodynamic argument at this point because we are about to consider kinetic processes where time scale becomes crucial. In this connection we may note that, in general, the rate at which a system comes to equilibrium depends directly on the temperature. The nature of the equilibrium state will also be temperature dependent.

The qualitative conclusion from the previous sentences is that the higher the temperature of a system, the more difficult it is to maintain states other than equilibrium states. We note that the application of thermodynamics to such obvious nonequilibrium processes as flames, rocket engines, etc., hinges on the very rapid establishment of local equilibria at high temperatures.

In order to maintain a nonequilibrium system we require the expenditure of energy. Consider the case where we do external work and convert an equilibrium system to a nonequilibrium state; the system if left will decay back to its initial equilibrium condition. The same reasoning applies if continuous work is done on the system; some of the energy will decay into thermal modes so that a steady expenditure of energy is necessary to maintain the nonequilibrium state. The rate at which we have to perform work to maintain a nonequilibrium state will depend on the rate of decay. Again, there is a general result that the decay toward equilibrium proceeds at a higher rate the higher the temperature, so that more energy flow is required to maintain nonequilibrium states in high-temperature than in low-temperature systems.

In any case, the maintenance of a nonequilibrium state of a system connected to an isothermal reservoir requires the expenditure of energy by a source capable of feeding energy into the system. The nonequilibrium condition of a system closed to the flow of matter requires an energy source, and the constant decay toward equilibrium requires a heat flow to an energy sink. Energy flow implies nonequilibrium and over an extended period of time, the condition of nonequilibrium requires energy flow, thus establishing the logical equivalence of energy flow and nonequilibrium over an extended time scale.

Energy flows can either be steady, periodic, or irregular. We will concentrate attention on the first two since they are simpler to deal with and correspond to the terrestrial models of energy flow which are our ultimate concern in this study. The energy sources might be mechanical, electromagnetic, thermal, or if the system is open to a flow of matter, it can be the stored potential energy of molecules.

We have already demonstrated that the steady flow of energy leads to material cycling in a system. If we take time averages in the periodic case, we can demonstrate similar but more complex cycling. Thus, maintaining a nonequilibrium system implies material cycles in the system. The features usually involved in functional complexity are connected with the cycling, while a related process in terms of covalent bonding leads to structural complexity. The functional and structural complexity are, as we shall see, closely related aspects of the flow of energy.

The next problem is to find a formal measure of how far a system is from equilibrium. First, consider a thermodynamic characterization of the systems being considered. If one deals with systems at constant volume and constant temperature, equilibrium is characterized by the minimum value of the Helmholtz free energy consistent with the constraints (see Appendix I). Therefore, all other states must correspond to a higher value for this parameter. We can, in general, characterize the distance of a given nonequilibrium state from its corresponding equilibrium state by

$$\text{Nonequilibrium character} = A_{\text{nonequilibrium}} - A_{\text{equilibrium}} \quad (6\text{-}13)$$

The measure as outlined is not completely unambiguous, since for a given nonequilibrium state, we must note the equilibrium state that we are using for comparison. There are three possibilities.

(a)   Surround the nonequilibrium system by an adiabatic envelope and let it decay to equilibrium. This final state would be the fiduciary state for comparison. The corresponding ensemble would be microcanonical.

(b)   Allow the nonequilibrium system to equilibrate with a reservoir at temperature T', which is the kinetic temperature of the nonequilibrium system. The equilibrated system would define the $A_{equilibrium}$. The corresponding ensemble is canonical.

(c)   Allow the system to equilibrate with a reservoir at temperature T, which is the temperature of the reservoir which serves as the actual energy sink in the flow that generated the nonequilibrium system. The ensemble representation is canonical in this case.

We could develop a measure using any of the three equilibrium conditions, but for reasons which we shall subsequently develop, we will choose case b, the system at the same kinetic temperature. We then have a perfectly well-defined measure of the distance from equilibrium of any nonequilibrium state. The measure is not restricted to systems undergoing energy flow but applies equally well to metastable systems slowly decaying to equilibrium.

The problem of defining $A_{nonequilibrium}$ becomes difficult in complex cases. In simple cases, consider Fig. 6-4. Under normal equilibrium conditions the partition function is completely dominated by the collection of low-lying states B. The Helmholtz free energy is obtained directly from the partition function of B and is given by $A_B = -kT \ln Z_B$. If the nonequilibrium ensemble is dominated by systems represented by A, the upper-lying energy levels, then $A_A = -kT \ln Z_A$. In principle, we could measure the distance from equilibrium for any system by knowing the distribution between A and B and the kinetic temperature T'. For the simple case just discussed, the measure of the distance from equilibrium is similar to the affinity as used in irreversible thermodynamics (15). Its actual physical measurement is approachable by the methods of thermodynamics.

We now come to defining order in a way that will accord with our biological intuition, will be physically meaningful, and will, hopefully, be of heuristic value. There are in biology two levels of order; that concerned with molecular events and that concerned with large-scale events, such as the pattern on butterfly wings or the pecking order in a flock of chickens. These two aspects of order are clearly related although tracing the relationships remains a future problem. The molecular order involves far more energy and relates itself more easily to physical theory. As Morrison (5) has noted, "Nearly all the manifest visual and mechanical intricacy of organisms, like their apt behavior, turns out to be without quantitative thermodynamic importance. Morphology and ecology are from the present point of view only small secondary properties of a fundamentally thermodynamic system." Our definition of order will

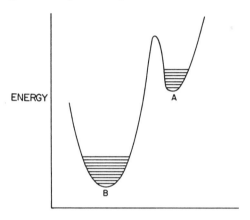

FIG. 6-4. Energy diagram of two isomers, one at an appreciably lower energy than the other.

thus deal more with the molecular aspect of the problem. From this molecular point of view, order must then be some monotonic function of the distance of the system from equilibrium. Let us summarize from our present point of view the properties of a system remaining at a point away from equilibrium.

(1) Energy must constantly be supplied and withdrawn to maintain the system.

(2) The macroscopic state of the system yields more detail about the microstates than for an equilibrium system.

(3) Material cycles occur within the system.

(4) The system is at a higher Helmholtz free energy than the corresponding equilibrium system at the same kinetic temperature.

Our assertion is then: in a thermodynamic system the only meaningful measure of order is related to some measure of how far the system is from equilibrium. Since all isothermally connected systems tend to decay to equilibrium, maintenance of order requires continued energy flow. This energy flow inevitably produces cycles automatically associating a functional order with any structural order that we wish to specify. The next task is to decide the function that we wish to use to measure order. The requirement that has been set forth is that it is a monotonic increasing function of $(A_{nonequil} - A_{equil})$, a quantity we will denote as $\Delta A(T')$ to indicate that the difference is being taken at the same kinetic temperature. The order function introduced in Chapter I and designated the L function is

$$L = \frac{\Delta A(T')}{kT'} \tag{6-14}$$

The particular choice has the following properties:

(1) It has a zero value for equilibrium systems.

(2) It fits our intuitive notions which identify order with distance from equilibrium.

(3) It is dimensionless.

(4) It makes contact with probability theory and information theory as will be demonstrated.

As we have already noted, knowing that a system is in a particular nonequilibrium state gives us more information about the microstate it is in than does the corresponding equilibrium state. The quantity $1.44\, L$ measures the increase in information about the microstate.

Thus far in this chapter we have formulated the order problem without specific reference to the structure of the system in terms of chemical species, or even without specific reference to the atomicity of the components. When we include these features, a number of new results follow which make contact with biology. We will first list these and then discuss them.

(a) Energy in different modes contributes to the organization in different ways.

(b) For each chemical system a maximum possible degree of order exists.

(c) Over a certain range, order in the abstract thermodynamic sense corresponds to complexity in molecular structure as well as to the nature of the processes taking place.

(d) The structure of the system depends in a very detailed way on the energy source and the geometry of the source–sink system.

In our previous discussion we referred to the kinetic temperature of the system. In accordance with the usage of Chapman and Cowling (16), we have identified this with the kinetic energy of the atoms in the system. For equilibrium systems the kinetic temperature is identical with the absolute thermodynamic temperature. For most nonequilibrium systems the kinetic temperature is what we would measure with a perfect gas thermometer or an equivalent empirical thermometer which was in contact with the system through rigid diathermal walls. In general, the kinetic temperature reflects the translational, vibrational, and rotational energy of a system; those modes into which energy equipartitions in equilibrium cases. The general criterion for energy to equipartition is that the degree of freedom under consideration enters the Hamiltonian as a square term and the energy levels are closely spaced compared with kT. The conditions are, in general, fulfilled by kinetic degrees of freedom and in the case of vibrational energy, it is usually fulfilled by the potential energy term. The crucial feature about these degrees of freedom is that energy very rapidly partitions among them in a Maxwell–Boltzmann fashion so that we can always consider a kind of local equilibrium existing, thus giving temperature a meaning in nonequilibrium cases.

In addition to this kinetic energy, the internal energy includes terms involving the potential energy of atomic and molecular interactions as well as mechanical and electrical contributions. These modes of energy dissipate more slowly into a Maxwell–Boltzmann distribution, contributing in the interim to the internal energy and thus to the Helmholtz free energy of the nonequilibrium system. It is these nonthermal energy storage terms which provide the basis for what we usually designate as organization. In the usual biological cases these energy terms consist of the potential energy of covalent bonds which lie above the minimum free energy configuration of the system.

It is now possible to see in molecular detail why the flux of energy is an organizing factor. In order for energy to flow from the source into the system, the source must be at a higher kinetic temperature. Upper-lying energy levels in the intermediate system will become populated and these take a finite time to decay into thermal modes. During this period, energy is stored in the upper states and the system is at a higher Helmholtz free energy than at equilibrium, leading to a nonzero L function and an ordered configuration. This process is quite general, but only produces chemical organization or complexity in a restricted number of cases.

From our analysis thus far, it is clear that the particular nonequilibrium state achieved will depend on the system, the source, and the sink. A full kinetic analysis is required to describe the final state and this is, of course, impossibly complicated. We intuitively feel that some as yet undiscovered principle will give more detail about the steady state without exhaustive kinetic analysis, but until such a principle appears, we can only give some qualitative arguments about the conditions required to achieve chemical complexity. First and foremost from the point of view of the system is atomic composition. A system consisting of a monatomic perfect gas cannot achieve a very high order measure. The only potential energy that can be stored is in excited electronic states and ions. These, however, decay very rapidly toward the equilibrium state. The only way to maintain such a configuration is to pump a lot of energy into the system. However, pumping a lot of energy into the system increases the kinetic temperature since, in the steady state,

$$\text{Energy flow} = \Phi(T, T' - T) \qquad (6\text{-}15)$$

where the energy flow must be a single-valued monotonic increasing function of $T' - T$, the difference in temperature between the system and the sink. However, as the temperature rises, the reference equilibrium system more nearly resembles the excited system so that L does not rise very rapidly.

On the other hand, systems of chemical complexity that can form a large number of stable covalent, ionic, or metallic bonds can store a large amount of energy in such bonds. The key factor is the stability of the bonds. If they have a relatively long half-life, large amounts of energy can be stored and the system can achieve a high order measure.

A hydrodynamic analogy might be helpful at this point. Consider a cylinder inside a larger cylinder. The smaller cylinder has holes going up the side getting progressively larger, and the large cylinder has one hole at the bottom. The whole system sits in a very, very large pan with a constant height of liquid (see Fig. 6-5). In the equilibrium state with no flow, all three vessels have liquid at the same height. Now consider the case where liquid is pumped into the inner vessel at a fixed rate. At low rates the liquid in the inner vessel will rise quite rapidly, while the liquid in the middle vessel will rise more slowly. As the flow rate gets faster, the leak rate from the inner vessel begins to get large faster than the leak rate from the middle vessel, so that the water rises less steeply in the inner cylinder compared to the outer. Eventually at high enough flows, the outer and inner cylinders will be at the same height. In our analogy, the height of liquid in the very large pan corresponds to the temperature of the sink. The height of liquid in the outer cylinder corresponds to the kinetic temperature, and the difference in height between the inner and outer cylinders corresponds to the stored potential energy or the L function. The fact that the holes get larger along the cylinder corresponds to the fact that at sufficiently high potential energy, states become less stable. This analogy shows why the order measure goes through a maximum as a function of flow rate.

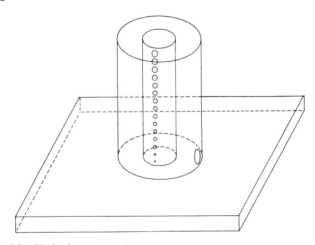

FIG. 6-5. Hydrodynamic analog for order measure L. Water flows in inner cylinder (chemical energy), then into outer cylinder (thermal energy), and finally into pan (thermal energy of the sink). L is analogous to the height of the inner cylinder minus the height of the outer cylinder. As the rate of flow into the inner cylinder increases, L goes through a maximum.

The reason for upper-lying potential states being inherently less stable can be seen in the following way. Any covalent bond has a finite probability of dissociating, giving rise to two free radicals. In stable compounds this takes place at a very slow rate and can be ignored. However, as we go to compounds of progressively higher potential bond energy, we are getting closer to the dissociated system and the rate of dissociation, which is proportional to

$$\frac{kT}{h} \exp\left(-\frac{\Delta F_d^{\ddagger}}{RT}\right)$$

where $\Delta F_d^{\ddagger}$ is the dissociation energy, will increase. It is thus a fundamental property of chemical systems that molecules which possess very high amounts of potential energy are inherently unstable to dissociation. This property alone places an upper limit on the order of systems in which the method of energy storage is chemical (see Fig. 6-6).

In these terms we can reexamine our order measure from a slightly different point of view. Suppose we multiply L in Eq. (6-14) by h which is Planck's constant. We get

$$L' = hL = \frac{\Delta A}{(kT/h)} \tag{6-16}$$

The order L' represents a ratio of an energy to a rate; the energy stored in the system in potential and entropic modes divided by a sort of universal rate constant (17) depicting the decay to equilibrium. Order

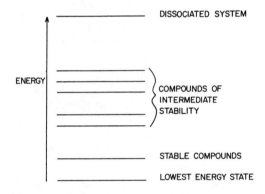

FIG. 6-6. Energy levels of various classes of compounds.

represents a kind of tension between storing energy and the decay of energy into the most random possible distribution.

The kind and degree of ordering will also depend on the nature of the source and sink. In general, the sink must be cold enough so that kT or kT' will be small compared to the quanta of energy which enter the system. If this is not the case, we will be dealing almost exclusively with energy which equipartitions in thermal modes so that no storage and no ordering occurs. For this reason, we would expect heat sources to be one of the least efficient methods for ordering. L as a function of heat flow probably has a lower maximum compared to other forms of energy flux.

Visible and ultraviolet radiation are probably, for most chemical systems, optimal ordering fluxes. The energy comes in quanta such that $h\nu$ is large compared to kT. The quanta are, however, the order of magnitude of energies involved in changing from one stable chemical configuration to another; hence, the amount of energy chemically stored can become large in such systems. In addition, the absorption is specific, due to the sharp character of molecular absorption spectra so that thermodynamically improbable selections of molecules can be made on the kinetic weighting due to these absorption spectra.

As one gets to quanta, which are as large as or larger than the dissociation energies (short ultraviolet, X-rays, γ-rays), one gets into modes which are less efficient for ordering, since the dissociated products undergo very exothermic reactions, rapidly converting the energy into thermal modes. The optimal sources for chemical ordering must be those for which $h\nu \cong \langle \Delta F^{\pm} \rangle_{av}$ for the possible chemical reactions in the system. It is part of the "fitness of the environment" that solar flux and carbon chemistry have an excellent match in this regard.

The form of Eq. (6-16) suggests an interesting analogy to an equation associated with mass flow through a system. If a system stores an amount of material M and maintains a flux of material $\mathscr{F}$, then if the flowing material is free to exchange with the stored material, the average amount of time that material spends in the system is given by

$$\bar{t} = \frac{M}{\mathscr{F}} \qquad (6\text{-}17)$$

By analogy, L' relates to the average amount of time that energy spends in the system on its way from the source to the sink. The more organized the system, the longer energy is stored. Since there is no way to provide "tracers" for energy, there is no operational way to give meaning to the previous sentence. In present-day terrestrial biology, the flow of energy is always linked to the flow of carbon so that $\bar{t}$ becomes measurable, and ecological organization can be viewed in terms of Eqs. (6-16) and (6-17) as we have already noted in Chapter III. Margelef (18) has noted that "An ecosystem that has a complex structure, rich in information, needs a lower amount of energy for maintaining such structure... . This seems to be one of the basic principles of ecology, probably recognized tacitly by most writers, although rarely put in an explicit way." Equation (6-16) expresses the same thought. A highly organized system, high L', maintains a small energy flow (kT'/h) relative to its size (ΔA). Thus, in one sense at least, our definition of order makes contact with ecology.

We have previously noted that the thermodynamic definition of order relates to notions of complexity in relation to macromolecular structure. That is, we would expect systems of complex macromolecules to show a substantial L measure so that the measure accords with our intuitive notions of order in biology.

Consider a system containing the elements CHNO with a kinetic temperature of 25°C. At equilibrium we have noted that such a system will be dominated by CO_2, N_2, and H_2O, and will, of course, have an order measure zero. To increase L at the same kinetic temperature, we must chemically rearrange bonds to yield a system of higher potential energy. In Table 6-2 we write down and classify the possible bonds in the CHNO system.

TABLE 6-2

CHAIN-TERMINATING AND CHAIN-EXTENDING BONDS IN
EQUILIBRIUM AND NONEQUILIBRIUM SYSTEMS

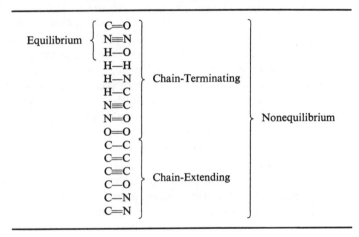

Bonds may be classified as chain-terminating or chain-extending. If they give rise to a structure that can add on at both ends they are chain-extending. The equilibrium distribution is dominated by chain-terminating bonds. This is not a thermodynamic necessity but is a property of the particular atoms involved. For the CHNO system it leads to an equilibrium configuration of rather low average molecular weight. As we raise the stored energy at constant T', we must begin to sample some of the higher energy bonds, both the chain-extending and the chain-terminating ones. Certain of the chain-extending bonds, such as C—C and C—N, are stable under ordinary conditions and thus make an important contribution to the system. Thus as L increases, average molecular size increases due to the accumulation of chain extending bonds. Note again, this is a result of the chemical thermodynamics of CHNO and need not apply to systems made up of other atoms.

The existence of chain-extending bonds increases L for another reason. The function has a ΔS as well as a ΔU part, and the ΔS is, in general, lowered by chain formation leading to a positive value of $-T\Delta S$ and an increase in L. In ordinary biological systems, order as thermodynamically defined corresponds to macromolecular complexity.

The previous arguments allow us to see the beginnings of a principle of maximum order; a principle which tells us where evolution is going. We will argue qualitatively and for a single case that a system tends toward the maximum L consistent with the constraints. Consider again a CHNO system at equilibrium in contact with a thermal reservoir. At equilibrium, CO_2, N_2, and H_2O dominate the system and the order measure is zero. Next, begin to irradiate the system with a constant source of monochromatic photons. A series of photochemical reactions begins leading to a large group of intermediate compounds. These intermediates must of necessity have a higher Helmholtz free energy than the ground state so that L rises. Some of these intermediates will have very short half-lives and will rapidly decay, while others will persist for longer periods, leading to a building up of concentrations of the more persistent ones. These species can enter into further photochemical processes, going into even higher free energy intermediates. At all stages there is constant selection for the most stable intermediates. The more stable the intermediates, the higher the $\bar{t}$ and the larger the L'. The selection for stability plus the constant pumping by energy flow will lead to the largest possible stored energy and the largest degree of order.

If this principle is general it means that the steady state is that energy flow state which maintains the system maximally far from equilibrium. Nonequilibrium states become conceptually very different from equilibrium states. If the biosphere is that system which maximizes L for the terrestrial surface, it becomes a necessary state of the system rather than an accidental one.

Having come this far in our view of the living process, one is tempted to speculate about meaning in biology, about the role of the individual in the biosphere, and about related questions of philosophical interest. But I am reminded that at the outset I promised that this book would deal with science, so I must leave each reader to his own metaphysical and theological conclusions.

References

1. L. Brillouin, "Science and Information Theory," 2nd ed. Academic Press, New York, 1962.
2. L. Szilard, *Z. Physik* **53**, 840 (1929).
3. M. W. Zemansky, "Heat and Thermodynamics." McGraw-Hill, New York, 1957.
4. E. Schrödinger, "What Is Life?" Cambridge Univ. Press, London and New York, 1945.
5. P. Morrison, *Rev. Mod. Phys.* **36**, 517 (1964).
6. N. Bohr, *Nature* **131**, 421 (1933).
7. N. Bohr, *Nature* **131**, 457 (1933).
8. W. Elsasser, "Atom and Organism." Princeton Univ. Press, Princeton, New Jersey, 1966.
9. J. Platt, *Science* **146**, 347 (1964).
10. H. J. Morowitz and R. C. Cleverdon, *Radiation Res.* **13**, 854 (1960).
11. R. B. Setlow and E. C. Pollard, "Molecular Biophysics." Addison-Wesley, Reading, Massachusetts, 1962.
12. M. Gell-Mann, personal communication, 1966.
13. E. T. Jaynes, *Phys. Rev.* **106**, 620 (1957).
14. H. B. Callen, "Thermodynamics." Wiley, New York, 1963.
15. I. Prigogine, "Thermodynamics of Irreversible Processes." Charles C. Thomas, Springfield, Illinois, 1955.
16. S. Chapman and T. G. Cowling, "The Mathematical Theory of Non-Uniform Gases." Cambridge Univ. Press, London and New York, 1939.
17. S. Glasstone, K. J. Laidler, and H. Eyring, "The Theory of Rate Processes." McGraw-Hill, New York, 1941.
18. R. Margelef, *in* "Readings in Ecology" (E. J. Kormondy, ed.). Prentice-Hall Englewood Cliffs, New Jersey, 1965.

APPENDIX I

Brief Summary of Some Points of Importance from Thermal Physics

Thermodynamics, statistical mechanics, and kinetic theory deal with those aspects of experience where the number of degrees of freedom becomes so large that detailed description of the behavior of all parts of the system becomes impossible, and we are forced to formulate our arguments in terms of integral or average properties. The primary quantity in all such analysis is energy, and all formulations and parameters relate more or less closely to energy measures.

The starting point in much of thermodynamics is the total energy U. For equilibrium systems, the total energy of homogeneous phases is a function of the volume entropy and mole numbers only. Changes in U between different states of the system are always measurable in mechanical equivalents. U is, however, only precisely measurable in adiabatically isolated systems, since in all other systems, energy can exchange with surroundings and fluctuations can occur. Statistical mechanics begins with the assumption that the energy eigenvalue at any instant has a precise value ϵ_i and that, ideally, the ϵ_i are available from mechanics or, more precisely, quantum mechanics. The assumption is then made that the measured value of U is a time average of ϵ_i values over the time of measurement. The further assumption is made that, at equilibrium, we can assign perfectly definite probabilities of the system being in the ith state so that

$$U = \bar{\epsilon} = \sum f_i \epsilon_i \tag{1}$$

We thus have a well-defined correspondence between the total energy terms in thermodynamics and statistical mechanics. The total energy U also has meaning for nonequilibrium systems since such systems can be adiabatically isolated and allowed to age into an equilibrium state where U is measurable.

The total energy of the system may change in a large number of ways. The usual statement of the first law of thermodynamics includes changes

148

due to heat flow and pressure-volume work. The change in total energy can, in general, be represented by a number of terms of the form

$$dU = dQ - p\,dV + \sigma\,dA + \psi\,de$$
$$+ \sum \mu_i\,dn_i + \chi\,dl + G\,dm \qquad (2)$$

The first term on the right represents the microscopic energy transfers, while all the subsequent terms represent macroscopic quantities of mechanics, electricity, and chemistry. The particular terms represented in Eq. (2) are pressure-volume work, surface-tension area work, electrical work, compositional change, tension-length work, and a gravitational energy term.

Temperature enters thermal physics from a number of independent but closely related concepts. The ultimate consistency of all of these various "temperatures" provides part of the validation of the various approaches. Empirical thermometers start with the physiological notions of hot and cold as related to any physical property that changes in a systematic way with hotness or coldness. An empirical thermometer measures temperature as proportional to that property, the best-known case being the gas thermometer which defines temperature as

$$T = \left(\frac{1}{R}\right)pV \qquad (3)$$

The proportionality constant $1/R$ depends upon the value assigned to the temperature fixed point. Different empirical thermometers do not as a rule agree at temperatures other than the fixed point. The most widely used fixed point is the triple point of water which is assigned the value 273.16.

Absolute thermodynamic temperature, or Kelvin temperature, is defined in terms of the efficiency of Carnot engines and involves an elaborately constructed series of definitions and proofs. It is independent of the working substance of the engine and introduces the concept of absolute zero in a very natural way. For empirical thermometers made up of gases whose energy U is a function of the temperature only, it may be shown that the empirical temperature is equal to the Kelvin absolute thermodynamic temperature.

From the postulational point of view, we can define temperature as one of the intensive variables of the system, being equal to

$$T = \left(\frac{\partial U}{\partial S}\right)_{V,N_1,N_2,N_3} \qquad (4)$$

This definition can be shown to yield the same measure as the Kelvin absolute thermodynamic temperature. The approach is closely related to that of Carathéodory who introduced $1/T$ as an integrating factor for dQ and then showed that temperature so defined has all the usual properties. Such a procedure simultaneously introduces entropy and temperature.

We may define kinetic temperature as being equal to a constant multiplied by the average kinetic energy per atom in the system. At equilibrium, it can be shown that the kinetic temperature is equal to the absolute thermodynamic temperature. Kinetic temperature and empirical temperature can be defined locally and for nonequilibrium systems, whereas the other definitions of temperature apply at equilibrium and as state variables of the entire system.

The third quantity of importance in thermal physics is entropy. This parameter may also be introduced from a number of points of view, and understanding the relation between them is part of the intellectual framework of thermal physics. In classical thermodynamics, entropy is introduced as the integral of dQ/T, where dQ is defined from a consideration of the equivalence of work and heat, and T is the absolute thermodynamic temperature. In the postulational approach to thermodynamics, entropy is introduced as that function of the extensive variables U, V, N_1, N_2, ..., N_n which is maximized at equilibrium.

In statistical mechanics, entropy is a property of the ensemble of systems used to represent the actual system. Three types of ensembles are commonly used: the microcanonical, the canonical, and the grand canonical.

(a) *Microcanonical ensemble.* A collection of systems, each possessing the same volume, chemical composition, and energy as the system of interest. To insure the energy condition, members of the microcanonical ensemble must be surrounded by adiabatic walls.

(b) *Canonical ensemble.* A collection of systems, each possessing the same volume, chemical composition, and average temperature as the system of interest. This is a collection of chemically and volumetrically identical systems in contact with a very large isothermal reservoir through rigid impermeable diathermal walls.

(c) *Grand canonical ensemble.* The condition for forming a grand canonical ensemble permits fluctuations in the mole numbers as well as the energy. It is thus a collection of systems of the same volume in contact with a large isothermal chemical reservoir of constant composition through rigid, diathermal, permeable walls.

Using any of the ensembles it is possible, in principle, in either classical physics or quantum mechanics, to describe all possible states of the ensemble members. In quantum mechanics these solutions are characterized by energy eigenvalues ϵ_i. We designate by n_i the number of ensemble members in the ith state at equilibrium. The first problem of statistical mechanics is to determine the n_i and to calculate all quantities of interest from the distribution of the n_i. This should yield appropriate averages consistent with macroscopic measurement. If we designate $n_i/\sum n_i$ as f_i, we then find that the most probable distribution of the n_i is the one that maximizes the quantity $-\sum f_i \ln f_i$. It is then possible to show that in order to make statistical mechanics and thermodynamics consistent, it is necessary that

$$S = -k \sum f_i \ln f_i \tag{5}$$

and

$$f_i = \frac{\exp(-\epsilon_i/kT)}{\sum \exp(-\epsilon_i/kT)}$$

$$= \frac{\exp(-\epsilon_i/kT)}{Z} \tag{6}$$

where Z is the partition function. In Chapter VI an alternative approach is discussed in which an equation equivalent to Eq. (5) is introduced from an information theory point of view.

From the fundamental quantities introduced, a number of energy functions are derived. The most commonly used of these are the enthalpy, the Helmholtz free energy, and the Gibbs free energy which are defined as

$$\text{Enthalpy:} \quad H = U + pV$$

$$\text{Helmholtz free energy:} \quad A = U - TS$$

$$\text{Gibbs free energy:} \quad F = U + pV - TS$$

The enthalpy is particularly useful in thermochemistry, since the heat given off or taken up in a constant pressure reaction is equal to the enthalpy change ΔH. The Helmholtz free energy is of use in relating thermodynamic and statistical mechanical quantities for a canonical ensemble, since it can be shown that

$$A = -kT \ln Z \tag{7}$$

The Gibbs free energy is particularly useful in studying chemical equilibrium problems at constant temperature and pressure. For multicomponent systems the Gibbs free energy relates simply to the chemical potentials by the relationship

$$F = \sum \mu_i n_i \tag{8}$$

Other energy functions may be introduced for special purposes.

The equilibrium condition is usually formulated by minimizing the Gibbs free energy or the Helmholtz free energy. The particular choice of energy function depends upon the constraints in a given situation.

The most general determination of equilibrium is made by maximizing the entropy of a system and the rest of the universe in contact with it. The condition of equilibrium is therefore

$$dS = dS_{\text{system}} + dS_{\text{universe}} = 0 \tag{9}$$

The most general criterion of irreversibility is that the preceding quantity increases. For a system in contact with an isothermal reservoir, the second term can only be of the form of $-dQ/T$, where dQ is the flow of heat from the system to the reservoir; it is negative if heat flows into the reservoir (exothermic process) and positive if heat flows from the reservoir into the system (endothermic process). For a system at constant volume and closed to the flow of matter, $dQ_{\text{system}} = dU_{\text{system}}$. Hence, Eq. (9) can be expressed entirely in terms of state variables of the system and becomes

$$dS = dS_{\text{system}} - \frac{dU_{\text{system}}}{T} = 0 \tag{10}$$

The Helmholtz free energy A is equal to $U - TS$. At constant temperature

$$dA = dU - T\,dS \tag{11}$$

so that maximizing the global entropy is equivalent to minimizing the Helmholtz free energy of the system, as can be seen by comparing Eqs. (10 and (11).

In the usual biochemical writings, another free energy function is used, appropriate to systems at constant temperature and pressure. It is the Gibbs free energy and is defined as

$$F = U + pV - TS \tag{12}$$

At constant temperature and pressure,

$$dF = dQ - T\,dS \tag{13}$$

so that maximizing the entropy of the system and environment is equivalent to minimizing the Gibbs free energy of the system.

APPENDIX II

The Steady State of a Perfect Gas during Heat Flow. Prepared by Narendra S. Goel

In this appendix the distribution of number density $n(x)$, temperature $T(x)$, and pressure $p(x)$ will be determined for a model system which consists of a plane isothermal reservoir at temperature T_1 as the source of energy and a similar reservoir at temperature T_2 ($T_2 < T_1$) as the sink. A perfect monatomic gas is sandwiched as an infinite-plane slab between them. The direction perpendicular to the planes will be taken as the x direction as in Fig. AII-1. Clearly, the gradients in temperature, density,

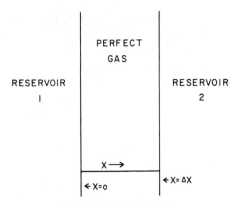

FIG. AII-1. Two-reservoir flow system with an intermediate perfect gas.

and pressure will be in one dimension only and the system will be in a nonequilibrium state, due to the flow of energy. To study such a state we have to make use of nonequilibrium statistical mechanics (*1*), nonequilibrium thermodynamics (*2*), and kinetic theory of gases (*3*, *4*); in particular, the Boltzmann transport equation. We will use the form of the Boltzmann transport equation which describes the behavior of the one-particle velocity distribution function (or equivalently, momentum distribution function). The background material for this type of approach

153

has been extensively treated in Chapman and Cowling (3) and Hirschfelder et al. (4).

Let $f(\mathbf{v}, \mathbf{r}, t)$ denote the one-particle distribution function in position ($\mathbf{r}$) and velocity ($\mathbf{v}$) space. Thus, $f(\mathbf{v}, \mathbf{r}, t)\, d\mathbf{r}\, d\mathbf{v}$ is the number of particles with space coordinates in the range $d\mathbf{r}$ around $\mathbf{r}$ and velocity coordinates in the range $d\mathbf{v}$ around $\mathbf{v}$. The Boltzmann equation satisfied by f in the absence of external fields is (4, p. 466)

$$\frac{\partial f}{\partial t} + \mathbf{v} \cdot \nabla f = \Gamma(\mathbf{v}, \mathbf{r}, t) \tag{1}$$

where ∇ stands for the gradient in position space and $\mathbf{r}$ denotes the rate of change of f caused by collisions with other particles. We further assume that the gas is sufficiently dilute so that there are only binary collisions present. In this case, Γ has the form (4, p. 449),

$$\Gamma = \int \sigma(g, \Omega)[f(\mathbf{v}'')f(\mathbf{v}''') - f(\mathbf{v})f(\mathbf{v}')]\, d\Omega\, d\mathbf{v}' \tag{2}$$

where $g \equiv |\mathbf{v} - \mathbf{v}'|$ is the relative velocity between the two particles moving with velocity $\mathbf{v}$ and $\mathbf{v}'$ respectively. They scatter from each other with an angle of scattering Ω and final velocities of $\mathbf{v}''$ and $\mathbf{v}'''$. The cross section describing the scattering is σ and $f(\mathbf{v})$ is the abbreviation of $f(\mathbf{v}, \mathbf{r}, t)$.

A number of quantities will now be defined which will be used in the subsequent discussion. The number density n at position $\mathbf{r}$ and time t is

$$n(\mathbf{r}, t) = \int f(\mathbf{v}, \mathbf{r}, t)\, d\mathbf{v} \tag{3}$$

The average velocity of a molecule is

$$\mathbf{v}_0 = \frac{1}{n} \int \mathbf{v} f(\mathbf{v}, \mathbf{r}, t)\, d\mathbf{v}$$

$$= \langle \mathbf{v}(\mathbf{r}, t) \rangle_{av} \tag{4}$$

The peculiar velocity of a molecule is

$$\mathbf{V} = \mathbf{v} - \mathbf{v}_0 \tag{5}$$

The energy per gram is

$$U(\mathbf{r}, t) = \frac{1}{mn} \int \left(\frac{1}{2} m \mathbf{V}^2 \right) f(\mathbf{v}, \mathbf{r}, t)\, d\mathbf{v} \tag{6}$$

The mass flux vector $\mathbf{J}_m$ is related to $\mathbf{V}$ by

$$\mathbf{J}_m = nm\mathbf{V} \tag{7}$$

and the energy flux is given by

$$\mathbf{q}(\mathbf{r}, t) = \int (\tfrac{1}{2}m\mathbf{V}^2)\mathbf{V}f(\mathbf{v}, \mathbf{r}, t)\, d\mathbf{V} \tag{8}$$

From Eqs. (3)–(8) it is clear that if we know the distribution functions, we can determine the mass and heat fluxes and, hopefully, by using the steady state condition and the condition of no mass flow, we should be able to determine the various distributions of interest.

The Boltzmann equation (1), along with the collision integral (2), is an integrodifferential equation and only an approximation method is available to solve it. The procedure, known as the Chapman–Enskog method, essentially involves a perturbation calculation. Here it is assumed that the system is not too far from equilibrium so that the leading term in the perturbation expansion for the distribution is the Maxwell–Boltzmann distribution function

$$f^0(\mathbf{v}, \mathbf{r}, t) = n(\mathbf{r}, t)\left[\frac{m}{2\pi kT(\mathbf{r}, t)}\right]^{3/2}\exp\left[-\frac{1}{2}\frac{m\mathbf{V}^2(\mathbf{r}, t)}{kT(\mathbf{r}, t)}\right] \tag{9}$$

and the actual distribution function is

$$f = f^0(1 + \Phi)(\mathbf{v}, \mathbf{r}, t) \tag{10}$$

where Φ is a small quantity denoting the perturbation. Equation (10) is substituted into Eqs. (1) and (2) and the equation obtained is solved for f subject to the auxiliary conditions

$$\int f^0\Phi\, d\mathbf{v} = 0 \tag{11a}$$

$$\int m\mathbf{v}f^0\Phi\, d\mathbf{v} = 0 \tag{11b}$$

$$\int \tfrac{1}{2}m\mathbf{V}^2 f^0\Phi\, d\mathbf{v} = 0 \tag{11c}$$

These equations describe the conservation of mass, momentum, and energy in the system. The conservation conditions can be obtained from the Boltzmann equation [Eq. (1)] by multiplying it by m, $m\mathbf{V}$, and

$\frac{1}{2}mV^2$ respectively and then integrating over $\mathbf{v}$. If we restrict the analysis to gradients in the x direction only, the equations thus obtained are

$$\frac{\partial n}{\partial t} + \frac{\partial}{\partial x}(nv_{0x}) = 0 \tag{12a}$$

$$\frac{\partial(v_{0x})}{\partial t} + v_{0x}\frac{\partial v_{0x}}{\partial x} = -\frac{1}{mn}\frac{\partial p}{\partial x} \tag{12b}$$

$$\frac{3}{2}nk\left(\frac{\partial T}{\partial t} + v_{0x}\frac{\partial T}{\partial x}\right) = -\frac{\partial q}{\partial x} - p\frac{\partial v_{0x}}{\partial x} \tag{12c}$$

where v_{0x} is the x component of v_0 and p is the ordinary hydrostatic pressure. Note that the contribution of the collision integral drops out in all these cases because mass, momentum, and energy are conserved in the collisions. For the steady state of the system where there is no mass flow, $\mathbf{v}_0$ vanishes, $\mathbf{V} = \mathbf{v}$, and all the time derivatives are zero. Equations (12) then become

$$\frac{\partial p}{\partial x} = 0, \quad \frac{\partial q}{\partial x} = 0 \tag{13}$$

The pressure and energy flow are both constant as a function of x. Further, it can be shown (4, p. 469) that Φ depends only on dT/dx so that q depends only on the temperature gradient and not on the density gradient. The exact dependence (4, p. 483) is

$$q = -\kappa T^{1/2}\frac{dT}{dx} \tag{14}$$

where κ is a constant which depends on molecular details such as shape and the nature of the interaction between them. Physically, one might expect a $T^{1/2}$ dependence because average molecular velocity varies as the square root of the temperature and the faster the molecules move, the greater the heat flux. In the following analysis it is not necessary to have the exact value of κ, which can always be determined experimentally from measured values of thermal conductivity. Equation (14) can be integrated to give

$$qx = \frac{2}{3}\kappa[T_1^{3/2} - T^{3/2}] \tag{15}$$

where use has been made of the boundary condition $T(0) = T_1$. Eq. (15) can be rewritten to give

$$T = T_1(1 - \beta x)^{2/3} \tag{16}$$

where

$$\beta = \frac{3}{2} \frac{q T_1^{-3/2}}{\kappa}$$

Since $T(\Delta x) = T_2$ where Δx is the distance between the source and the sink, Eq. (15) yields

$$q = \frac{2\kappa}{3\Delta x}(T_1^{3/2} - T_2^{3/2}) \tag{17}$$

so that the quantity β is given by

$$\beta = \frac{[1 - (T_2/T_1)^{3/2}]}{\Delta x} = \frac{(1 - \xi^3)}{\Delta x} \tag{18}$$

where

$$\xi = \left(\frac{T_2}{T_1}\right)^{1/2}$$

Utilizing the perfect gas relation in the form $p = nkT$ along with Eq. (16), we get

$$n = \frac{p}{kT_1}(1 - \beta x)^{-2/3} \tag{19}$$

If we use the remaining boundary condition

$$\int_0^{\Delta x} n\, dx = M \tag{20}$$

we get

$$M = \frac{3p}{RT_1\beta}[1 - (1 - \beta\Delta x)^{1/2}] \tag{21}$$

Using Eq. (18) this can be written

$$p = \frac{MRT_1}{3\Delta x}\frac{(1 - \xi^3)}{(1 - \xi)} \tag{22}$$

Thus, if T_1, T_2, Δx, and M are given, it is possible to calculate the energy flux, the density and temperature distribution functions, and the pressure.

We conclude Appendix II by making some general remarks about the tool we have used; namely, the Boltzmann equation. The Boltzmann equation (1), with the collision integral given by (2), is not valid for very high densities because at high densities, more than two-body collisions, which have been neglected in the derivation of (2), become important.

However, the Boltzmann equation is known to give results which agree very well with the experiments, even for the conditions for which its validity has been questioned due to the lack of its proper derivation. Further, it has been argued that the Chapman–Enskog solution of the Boltzmann equation, within the linear approximation, is sufficient for all purposes, for if it is not so, the Boltzmann equation, with the collision integral used in the previous discussion [Eq. (2)], itself is not valid. In the model system under consideration it is difficult to state explicitly the conditions under which the Chapman–Enskog solution is sufficient. But, perhaps, it is fair to say that the higher the temperature gradients, the less chance for the validity of the Chapman–Enskog solution and the Boltzmann equation with the collision integral given by (2). But this need not overly discourage us; again, due to the reasons mentioned earlier.

In any case, the detailed treatment confirms the result outlined in the Knudsen treatment and shows how order arises from energy flow, even for very simple systems.

References

1. I Prigogine, "Non-Equilibrium Statistical Mechanics." Wiley (Interscience), New York, 1962.

2. S. R. de Groot and P. Mazur, "Non-Equilibrium Thermodynamics." North-Holland, Amsterdam, 1962.

3. S. Chapman and T. G. Cowling, "The Mathematical Theory of Non-Uniform, Gases." Cambridge Univ. Press, London and New York, 1939.

4. J. O. Hirschfelder, C. F. Curtiss, and R. B. Bird, "Molecular Theory of Gases and Liquids." Wiley, New York, 1954.

APPENDIX III

Catalog of No-Carbon and One-Carbon Compounds of CHNOPS

NO-CARBON COMPOUNDS

$(HN)_n$	Imidogen polymer	$H_2N_2O_2$	Hyponitrous acid
HNO		$H_2N_2O_2$	Nitramide
HNOS	Sulfur oxide, oxime	$H_2N_2O_2$	Hyponitrous acid
HNOS	Thionyl imide	$H_2N_2O_5S$	Nitrosohydroxyl-
HNO_2	Nitrous acid		aminesulfonic acid
HNO_2S		$H_2N_2O_6$	
HNO_2S	Sulfimide	$H_2N_2O_9S$	
HNO_3	Peroxynitrous acid	$H_2N_2O_{15}S_3$	
HNO_3	Nitric acid	$H_2N_2O_{18}S_4$	
HNO_3S_8	Heptasulfuramidosul-	H_2N_2S	Sulfur imide
	fonic acid	$H_2N_4O_2S_6$	Tetrakis(thionitroso)-
HNO_4	Peroxynitric acid		dithionous acid
HNO_6S	Nitryl sulfate	$H_2N_4O_{10}$	
HNO_8S_2	Nitrosyl pyrosulfate	H_2O	Water
HNO_9S_2		H_2OS	Dihydrogen sulfoxide
HNO_9S_2	Nitryl pyrosulfate	H_2O_2	Hydrogen peroxide
$HNO_{12}S_3$		H_2OS	Dihydrogen sulfoxide
$HNO_{12}S_3$	Nitryl trisulfate	H_2O_2S	Sulfoxylic acid
$HNO_{15}S_4$	Nitryl tetrasulfate	$H_2O_2S_2$	Thiosulfurous acid
$HNO_{57}S_{18}$		$H_2O_3S_2$	Thiosulfuric acid
HNS	Sulfur imide	H_2O_4	Hydrogen superoxide
HNS_7	Heptasulfurimide	$H_2O_5S_2$	Pyrosulfurous acid
HN_2O_6S		$H_2O_6S_3$	Trithionic acid
HN_3OS_4	Tris(thionitroso)-	$H_2O_6S_4$	Tetrathionic acid
	sulfonium hydroxide	$H_2O_6S_5$	Pentathionic acid
HN	Pentazole	$H_2O_6S_6$	Hexathionic acid
HO_3		$H_2O_6S_7$	Heptathionic acid
HO_4		$H_2O_6S_8$	Octathionic acid
HPS_3	Phosphenotrithioic	$H_2O_6S_9$	Nonathionic acid
	acid	$H_2O_{10}S_3$	Trisulfuric acid
HS	Mercapto	$H_2O_{13}S_4$	Tetrasulfuric acid
H_2	Hydrogen	H_2S	Hydrogen sulfide
H_2NO		H_2S_2	Hydrogen sulfide
H_2NS_6		H_2S_3	Hydrogen sulfide
H_2N_2	Diimide	H_2S_4	Hydrogen sulfide

H_2S_5	Hydrogen sulfide
H_2S_6	Hydrogen sulfide
H_3NO_2S	
H_3NO_2S	Amidosulfurous acid
H_3NO_4S	Hydroxylamine-N-sulfonic acid
H_3NO_4S	Hydroxylamine-O-sulfonic acid
$H_3NO_4S_2$	Imidodisulfurous acid
$H_3NO_6S_2$	Imidodisulfuric acid
H_3NO_7S	
H_3NO_7S	Nitric acidium (1+) sulfate
$H_3NO_7S_2$	Hydroxylamine disulfonic acid
$H_3NO_{10}S_2$	Nitric acidium (1+) pyrosulfate
H_3N_2	Hydrazyl, polymer
$(H_3N_2)_n$	Hydrazyl, polymer
H_3N_2OP	Metaphosphimamide
H_3N_3	
$H_3N_3O_6S_3$	1,3,5,2,4,6-Trithiatriazine, 1,1,3,3,5,5-hexoxide
$H_3N_3O_9$	
$H_3N_3O_{12}S$	
$H_3N_3O_{21}S_4$	
$H_3N_3O_{24}S_5$	
H_3O_2P	Phosphinic acid
$H_3O_2PS_2$	Phosphorodithioic acid
H_3O_3P	Phosphonic acid
H_3O_3PS	Phosphorothioic acid
H_3O_5P	Peroxymonophosphoric acid
$H_3O_9P_3$	Metaphosphoric acid
H_3P	Hydrogen phosphide A
H_3PS_4	Phosphorotetrathioic acid
H_4N	Ammonium
H_4NO_3P	Ammonium metaphosphate
H_4NO_3P	Phosphoramidic acid
$H_4NO_8P_3$	Imidotrimetaphosphoric acid
H_4N_2	Hydrazine
$H_4N_2O_2$	Ammonium nitrite
$H_4N_2O_2S$	Hydrazinesulfinic acid

$H_4N_2O_2S$	Sulfamide
$H_4N_2O_2S$	Ammonium sulfimide
$H_4N_2O_2S_2$	
$H_4N_2O_3$	Ammonium nitrate
$H_4N_2O_3S$	Hydrazinesulfonic acid
$H_4N_2O_4$	Hydroxylamine nitrate
$H_4N_2O_4S_3$	Trithionamide
$H_4N_2O_8S_3$	Diimidotrisulfuric acid
$H_4N_2O_{11}S_2$	
$H_4N_2O_{25}S_6$	
$H_4N_3O_5S$	Dinitrososulfurous acid
$H_4N_4O_8S_4$	1,3,5,7,2,4,6,8-Tetrathiatetrazocine, 1,1,3,3,5,5,7,7-octaoxide
$H_4N_4O_{27}S_5$	
$H_4N_4O_{27}S_5$	
$H_4N_4S_4$	1,3,5,7,2,4,6,8-Tetrathiatetrazocine
$H_4O_5P_2$	Diphosphorous acid
$H_4O_5P_2$	Pyrophosphorous acid
H_4O_5S	
H_4O_5S	Oxonium sulfate
$H_4O_6P_2$	Hypophosphoric acid
$H_4O_6P_2$	Isohypophosphoric acid
$H_4O_6P_2S_2$	Thioperoxydiphosphoric acid
$H_4O_{12}P_4$	Metaphosphoric acid
$H_4O_{35}S_{11}$	
H_4P_2	Hydrogen phosphide B
H_5NO	Ammonium hydroxide
H_5NO_2	Ammonia compound with H_2O_2
H_5NO_2	Ammonium peroxide
H_5NO_3S	Ammonium bisulfite
H_5NO_4S	Ammonium bisulfate
$H_5NO_6P_2$	Imidodiphosphoric acid
$H_5NO_7S_2$	Ammonium pyrosulfate
$H_5NO_{11}S_2$	Nitric acidium (2+) sulfate
H_5NS	Ammonium sulfide, hydro
$H_5N_2O_2P$	Phosphorodiamidic acid

$H_5N_2O_7P_3$	Diimidotrimeta-phosphoric acid
$H_5N_3O_2S_2$	Imidodisulfurous diamide
$H_5N_3O_3$	Hydrazine nitrate
$H_5N_3O_4S_2$	Imidodisulfamide
H_5N_5	Hydrazine azide
$H_5N_5O_{10}S_5$	1,3,5,7,9,2,4,6,8,10-Pentathiapentazecine, 1,1,3,3,5,5,7,7,9,9-decaoxide
$H_5O_{10}P_3$	Triphosphoric acid
H_6NO_2P	Ammonium hydrophosphate
H_6NO_3P	Ammonium orthophosphite, di H
H_6NO_4P	Ammonium orthophosphate, di H
$H_6NO_9P_3$	Imidotriphosphoric acid
H_6N_2	Ammonium amide
H_6N_2O	Hydrazine hydrate
$H_6N_2O_2$	
$H_6N_2O_2S$	Ammonium amidosulfite
$H_6N_2O_2S_2$	Ammonium amidothiosulfate
$H_6N_2O_3S$	Ammonium hydroxylaminesulfonate
$H_6N_2O_3S$	Ammonium sulfamate
$H_6N_2O_5S_3$	Ammonium amidotrithionate
$H_6N_2O_{20}S_4$	
H_6N_3OP	Phosphoric triamide
$H_6N_3O_5P_3$	Metaphosphimic acid, trimer
H_6N_3PS	Phosphorothioic triamide
H_6N_4	Tetrazane
$H_6N_4O_6$	Hydrazine dinitrate
$H_6N_4O_9$	Ammonium nitrate
H_6O_4	
H_6O_6S	Orthosulfuric acid
$H_6O_{12}S_2$	Peroxymonosulfuric acid, compound with H_2O_2
$H_6O_{13}P_4$	Tetraphosphoric acid

$H_6O_{18}P_6$	Metaphosphoric acid
H_6P_{12}	Hydrogen phosphide C
$H_7NO_6P_2$	Ammonium hypophosphate
$H_7N_2O_3P$	Ammonium phosphoramidate
$H_7N_2O_4P$	Hydrazine orthophosphate
$H_7N_2O_4P$	Hydrazine monoorthophosphite
$H_7N_5O_{14}S_6$	Pentaimidohexasulfuric acid
H_7O_6P	
H_8N_2O	Ammonium oxide
$H_8N_2O_3S_2$	Ammonium thiosulfate
$H_8N_2O_4S$	Ammonium sulfate
$H_8N_2O_4S_2$	Ammonium dithionite
$H_8N_2O_5S$	Ammonium peroxymonosulfate
$H_8N_2O_6P_2$	Hydrazine hypophosphate
$H_8N_2O_6P_2$	Ammonium metaphosphate
$H_8N_2O_6S$	Hydroxalamine sulfate
$H_8N_2O_6S_3$	Ammonium trithionate
$H_8N_2O_6S_4$	Ammonium tetrathionate
$H_8N_2O_8S_2$	Ammonium peroxidisulfate
$H_8N_2O_{10}S_3$	Ammonium trisulfate
$H_8N_2O_{18}S_2$	
$H_8N_2O_{18}S_2$	Nitropersulfuric acid
$H_8N_2O_{24}S_5$	
H_8N_2S	Ammonium sulfide, mono
$H_8N_3O_2P$	Ammonium phosphorodiamidate
$H_8N_4O_4S_2$	Imidodisulfamide, ammonium derivative
$H_8N_4O_5S$	Ammonium nitrosohydroxylaminesulfonate
$H_9NO_8P_2$	Ammonium phosphate
$H_9N_2O_3PS$	Ammonium phosphorothioate

Formula	Name
$H_9N_2O_4P$	Ammonium orthophosphate, mono H
$H_9N_3O_4S_2$	Ammonium imidodisulfite
$H_9N_3O_6S_2$	Ammonium imidodisulfate
$H_9N_3O_7S_2$	Ammonium hydroxylamine disulfonate
$H_{10}N_2O_4S$	Ammonium sulfite
$H_{10}N_2O_6P_2$	Ammonium hydrophosphate
$H_{10}N_2O_6P_2$	Hydrazine diorthophosphate
$H_{10}N_2O_6S$	Ammonium sulfate, compound with H_2O_2
$H_{10}N_2O_7P_2$	Ammonium pyrophosphate
$H_{10}N_2O_7S_2$	Ammonium dithionate
$H_{10}N_4O_2S$	
$H_{10}N_4O_5S_2$	Pyrosulfamide, ammonium derivative
$H_{10}O_{26}S_7$	
$H_{11}N_3O_7S_2$	
$H_{12}N_3O_7P$	Hydroxylamine, phosphate
$H_{12}N_3O_9P_3$	Ammonium metaphosphate
$H_{12}N_4O_6S_2$	Ammonium imidodisulfate
$H_{12}N_4O_9S_3$	Ammonium nitridotrisulfate
$H_{12}N_4O_{10}P_4$	Metaphosphimic acid, tetramer, dihydrate
$H_{12}N_6O_6S_3$	1,3,5,2,4,6-Trithiatriazine hexaoxide, N-ammonium derivative
$H_{13}N_3O_8S_2$	Ammonium sulfate
$H_{13}N_5O_2S$	
$H_{14}N_6O_8P_4$	Ammonium metaphosphimate
$H_{15}N_3O_8P_2$	Ammonium phosphate
$H_{15}N_5O_6S_2$	
$H_{16}N_4O_7P_2$	Ammonium pyrophosphate
$H_{16}N_4O_{12}P_4$	Ammonium metaphosphate
$H_{16}N_6O_{10}S$	Ammonium nitrate sulfate
$H_{17}N_5O_4S$	
$H_{18}N_2O_{44}S_{10}$	
$H_{18}N_4O_{52}S_{11}$	
$H_{19}NO_{39}S_9$	
$H_{20}N_2O_{42}S_9$	
$H_{21}N_3O_{16}P_4$	Ammonium phosphate
$H_{24}N_9O_{13}P$	Ammonium nitrate phosphate
$H_{26}N_6O_{16}S_4$	Ammonium sulfate
$H_{28}N_{22}O_{78}S_3$	
$H_{30}N_7O_{12}P_3$	Ammonium phosphate
NO	Nitric oxide
NO_2	Nitrogen dioxide
NO_3	Nitrogen trioxide
NO_4	Nitrogen oxide
$(NS)_n$	Sulfur nitride
N_2OS_3	
N_2O_2	Nitrogen oxide
$N_2O_2S_3$	Trisulfur dinitrogen oxide
N_2O_3	Nitrogen sesquinonide
N_2O_5	Nitrogen pentoxide
$N_2O_5S_3$	Trisulfur dinitrogen pentoxide
$N_2O_5S_4$	
N_2O_9S	Nitrosylsulfuric acid
$N_2O_9S_2$	Nitrosyl pyrosulfate
$N_2O_{11}S_2$	Nitryl pyrosulfate
$N_2O_{12}S_3$	Nitrosyl trisulfate
$N_2O_{13}S_3$	Nitrosyl nitryl trisulfate
$N_2O_{14}S_3$	
$N_2O_{14}S_3$	Nitryl trisulfate
$N_2O_{17}S_4$	
$N_2O_{17}S_4$	Nitryl tetrasulfate
N_2S_2	Sulfur nitride
N_2S_4	Sulfur nitride
N_2S_5	Sulfur nitride
$N_3O_{10}P$	Phosphoryl nitrate
N_4O	Nitrosyl azide
$N_4O_6S_6$	Sulfur nitride, compound with SO_3
$N_4O_{12}S_8$	Sulfur nitride, compound with SO_3

$N_4O_{43}S_{11}$		$O_6P_4S_4$	Phosphorus oxysulfide
N_4S_4	Sulfur nitride	O_7S_2	Disulfur heptoxide
N_5P_3	Phosphorus nitride	$O_{10}P_6S_5$	Phosphorus oxysulfide
$N_{21}P_3$	Phosphonitrile azide, trimer	$O_{14}P_2S_3$	
O_2	Oxygen	P_2S_5	Phosphorus sulfide
OS_2	Disulfur monoxide	P_3S_6	Phosphorus sulfide
O_2S_2	Sulfur oxide	P_4S_5	Phosphorus sulfide
O_3S_2	Disulfur trioxide	P_4S_6	Phosphorus sulfide
O_4	Oxygen, tetratomic	P_4S_7	Phosphorus sulfide
O_4S	Sulfur tetroxide	P_4S_{10}	Phosphorus sulfide

ONE-CARBON COMPOUNDS

CHN	Hydrocyanic acid	CH_2N_4O	Tetrazol-5-ol
CHNO	Cyanic acid	CH_2N_4S	5-Amino-1,2,3,4-
CHNO	Fulminic acid		thiatriazole
$CHNO_2S$	Cyanosulfurous acid	CH_2N_6O	Azidoiminomethane-
$CHNO_3S$	Cyanosulfuric acid		diazonium hydroxide
CHNS	Thiocyanic acid	CH_2N_6O	Tetrazole-5-diazo-
CHNS	Isothiocyanic acid		hydroxide
CHN_3O_6	Nitroform	CH_2N_6O	Tetrazolediazonium
CHN_3S_2	Azidodithioformic acid		hydroxide
CHN_3S_2	Δ^2-1,2,3,4-Thiatri- azoline-5-thione	$CH_2N_6O_2$	1-Azido-N-nitro- formamidine
CHN_5	Pentazine	$CH_2N_6O_2$	5-Nitraminotetrazole
CHN_5O_2	Azidooxomethane-	CH_2O	Formaldehyde
	diazonium hydroxide	CH_2OS_2	Dithiocarbonic acid
CHO	Hydroxymethylidyne	CH_2O_2	Formic acid
CHO_2	Carboxy	CH_2O_2S	Thiocarbonic acid
CHO_2	Formyloxy	CH_2O_3	Peroxyformic acid
CHP	Methinophosphide	CH_2O_4	Peroxycarbonic acid
CH_2NO	Carbamoyl	CH_2S	Thioformaldehyde
CH_2N_2	Cyanamide	CH_2S_2	Dithioformic acid
CH_2N_2	Carbodiimide	CH_2S_3	Trithiocarbonic acid
CH_2N_2	Isodiazomethane	CH_3N	Methylenimine
$CH_2N_2O_3$	Formonitrolic acid	CH_3NO	Formamide
$CH_2N_2O_3$	Nitrolic acid	CH_3NO	Nitrosomethane
$CH_2N_2O_4$	Dinitromethane	CH_3NOS	Thiocarbamic acid
$CH_2N_2O_6$	Methylene nitrate	CH_3NOS	Thioformamide
$CH_2N_2O_6S_2$	Diazomethane-	CH_3NOS	N-Sulfinylmethylamine
	disulfonic acid	CH_3NOS	Methyl thionitrite
CH_2N_4	1,2,3,4-Tetrazole	CH_3NOS_7	
CH_2N_4O	Carbamoyl azide	CH_3NO_2	Nitromethane
CH_2N_4O	Tetrazole oxide	CH_3NO_2	Carbamic acid
CH_2N_4O	1-Hydroxytetrazole	CH_3NO_2	Formohydroxamic
CH_2N_4O	2-Tetrazolin-5-one		acid

CH_3NO_3	Methyl nitrate	$CH_4N_2O_2$	O-Carbamoyl-
CH_3NO_5S	Compound of sulfuric		hydroxylamine
	acid and fulminic	$CH_4N_2O_2$	N-Methyl-N-nitroso-
	acid		hydroxylamine
CH_3NO_5S	Nitromethanesulfanic	$CH_4N_2O_2$	Hydroxylamine
	acid		cyanate
CH_3NO_5S	Methyl nitrosylsulfate	$CH_4N_2O_2$	N-Nitromethylamine
CH_3NS	Thioformamide	$CH_4N_2O_2S$	Aminoiminomethane-
CH_3NS_2	Dithiocarbamic acid		sulfinic acid
CH_3N_3	Carbazonitrile	$CH_4N_2O_3S_2$	Ammonium thio-
CH_3N_3	Azidomethane		cyanatosulfonate
$CH_3N_3O_2S$	1-Nitro-2-thiourea	$CH_4N_2O_4S$	3-Sulfinocarbazic acid
$CH_3N_3O_2S$	Methanesulfonylazide	$CH_4N_2O_4S$	Ureasulfonic acid
$CH_3N_3O_3$	Nitrourea	CH_4N_2S	Thiourea
$CH_3N_3O_3$	Nitrocyanamide	CH_4N_2S	Ammonium isothio-
	hydrate		cyanate
CH_3N_5	1-Azideformamidine	CH_4N_2S	2-Thiopseudourea
CH_3N_5	5-Aminotetrazole	CH_4N_2S	Dithiocarbazic acid
CH_3O	Methoxy	CH_4N_4O	Nitrosoguanidine
CH_3O	Hydroxymethyl	$CH_4N_4O_2$	Nitroguanidine
CH_3OPS	Methylthionophos-	$CH_4N_4O_2$	Nitrocyanamide, NH_3
	phine oxide		derivative
CH_3O_2	Methyldioxy	$CH_4N_4O_4$	N,N'-Dinitromethane-
CH_3O_2PS	O-Methyl phospheno-		diamine
	thioate	$CH_4N_4O_6$	Nitroform, ammonium
CH_3O_5P	Formic acid anhydride		derivative
	with H_3PO_4	CH_4N_6	5-Hydrazinotetrazole
CH_3PS_3	Methyl phospheno-	CH_4O	Methanol
	trithioate	CH_4OP_2	Carbophosphide
CH_3S	Methyl thio	CH_4OS	Mercaptoethanol
CH_4	Methane	CH_4O_2	Methanediol
CH_4N	Methylamidogen	CH_4O_2	Methyl hydroperoxide
CH_4NO_5P	Carbamic acid	CH_4O_2S	Methane sulfinic acid
	anhydride with	$CH_4O_2S_2$	Methane sulfonic
	H_3PO_4		acid, thio
CH_4N_2	Formamidine	CH_4O_3	Hydroxymethyl
CH_4N_2	Ammonium cyanide		hydroperoxide
CH_4N_2O	Ammonium cyanate	CH_4O_3S	Methanesulfonic acid
CH_4N_2O	Formamidoxine	CH_4O_3S	Hydroxymethane-
CH_4N_2O	Ammonium isocyanate		sulfinic acid
CH_4N_2O	N-Hydroxyformami-	CH_4O_3S	Methyl sulfite
	dine	$CH_4O_3S_3$	Methyl thioperoxy-
CH_4N_2O	Methanediazonium		monosulfate
	hydroxide	CH_4O_4S	Methyl sulfuric acid
CH_4N_2O	N-Nitrosomethylamine	CH_4O_4S	Hydroxymethane-
$CH_4N_2O_2$	Hydroxyurea		sulfonic acid
$CH_4N_2O_2$	Carbazic acid	$CH_4O_6S_2$	Methionic acid

$CH_4O_7S_2$	Hydroxymethane disulfonic acid	CH_5O_2P	Methyl phosphinate
$CH_4O_8S_2$	Dihydroxymethane-disulfonic acid	CH_5O_3P	Methanephosphonic acid
$CH_4O_9S_3$	Methanetrisulfonic acid	CH_5O_3P	Methyl phosphite
		CH_5O_3P	Phosphinoorthoformic acid
CH_4P_2S	Thiocarbophosphide	CH_5O_3P	(Hydroxymethyl) phosphinic acid
CH_4S	Methanethiol		
CH_4S_2	Methanedithiol	CH_5O_3PS	Methyl phosphoro-thioate
CH_4S_2	Thiomethanesulfenic acid	CH_5O_4P	Methyl phosphate
CH_4S_3	Methyl hydrotrisulfide	CH_5O_4P	(Hydroxymethyl) phosphonic acid
CH_5N	Methylamine		
CH_5NO	Methylhydroxylamine	CH_5P	Methyl phosphine
CH_5NO	Aminomethanol	CH_6NO_2P	P-Methylphosphon-amidic acid
CH_5NO_2	Ammonium formate		
CH_5NO_3	Ammonium bicarbonate	CH_6NO_3P	(Aminomethyl) phosphonic acid
CH_5NO_2S	Aminomethane sulfinic acid	CH_6N_2	Methyl hydrazine
		CH_6N_2	Methanediamine
CH_5NO_2S	Methanesulfonamide	$CH_6N_2O_2$	Ammonium carbamate
CH_5NO_3S	Aminomethane sulfonic acid	$CH_6N_2O_2S$	Methanesulfonic acid hydrazide
CH_5NO_3S	Aminomethanol sulfite	$CH_6N_2O_2S$	Methylsulfamide
CH_5NO_3S	Methyl sulfamate	$CH_6N_2O_3$	Urea, compound with H_2O_2
CH_5NO_3S	Methyl sulfamic acid		
$CH_5NO_6S_2$	Methylimidodisulfuric acid	$CH_6N_2O_3S$	Hydrazinomethane-sulfonic acid
$CH_5NO_6S_2$	Aminomethane-disulfonic acid	$CH_6N_2O_4S_2$	N,N'-Methylenebis-amidosulfurous acid
$CH_5N_2O_3P$	(Aminomethylene) phosphoramidic acid	$CH_6N_2O_4S_2$	Diaminomethane-disulfinic acid
CH_5N_2S	Ammonium thiocyanate	$CH_6N_2O_6S_2$	Methanedisulfamic acid
CH_5N_3	Guanidine	$CH_6N_2S_2$	Ammonium dithio-carbamate
CH_5N_3O	Semicarbazide		
CH_5N_3O	Hydroxyguanidine	$CH_6N_3O_3P$	(Diaminomethylene) phosphoramidic acid
$CH_5N_3O_3S$	Amidinosulfamic acid		
$CH_5N_3O_3S$	Sulfamoylurea	$CH_6N_3O_3P$	Amidinophosphor-amidic acid
$CH_5N_3O_3S$	Thiourea nitrate		
$CH_5N_3O_4$	Urea nitrate	CH_6N_4	1-Amino guanidine
CH_5N_3S	Thiosemicarbazide	CH_6N_4O	Carbohydrazide
CH_5N_3S	Thiocyanic acid, com-pound with hydrazine	CH_6N_4S	Thiocarbohydrazide
		CH_6N_6	2-Tetrazene-1-carboxamidine
$CH_5N_5O_2$	1-Amino-3-nitro-guanidine	CH_6O_4	Formic acid, hydrate
		$CH_6O_6P_2$	Methylenediphos-phonic acid
CH_5OP	Methyl phosphinite		

CH_7NO_4S	Ammonium methyl sulfate	$CH_8N_4O_3S$	Guanidine, sulfamate
CH_7N_2OP	P-Methylphosphonic diamide	$CH_8N_4O_3S$	Sulfamoylurea, NH_3 derivative
CH_7N_2OP	Methyl phosphoro- diamidite	$CH_8N_4O_4$	Ammonium nitrate, compound with urea
$CH_7N_2O_2P$	Methyl phosphoro- diamidate	$CH_8N_4S_2$	Dithiocarbazic acid, hydrazine salt
$CH_7N_2O_5P$	Phosphoric acid, com- pound with urea	CH_8N_6	Triaminoguanidine
		CH_8N_8	1,3-Diaminoguanidine, hydrazoate
CH_7N_3	Methanetriamine	$CH_8N_8O_2$	5-Nitraminotetrazole,
CH_7N_3O	Guanidinium hydroxide		diammonium derivative
CH_7N_3O	Urea, compound with NH_3	CH_9N_9	1,2,3-Triamino- guanidine, hydrazo-
$CH_7N_3O_2$	Hydrazine, compound with nitromethane		ate
$CH_7N_3O_2$	N-aci-Nitromethyl- amine, ammonium derivative	$CH_{10}N_4O_3$	Hydrazine, carbonate
		$CH_{10}N_{10}O_2$	5-Nitraminotetrazole, compound with hydrazine
$CH_7N_3O_4S_2$	N-Methylimidodi- sulfamide	$CH_{11}N_2O_4P$	Ammonium methyl- phosphate
CH_7N_3S	Thiourea, compound with NH_3	$CH_{12}N_2O_9$	Urea, compound with H_2O_2
CH_7N_5	1,3-Diaminoguanidine	CNO	Cyanato
CH_7N_5	5-Aminotetrazolidine	CNO	Isocyanato
CH_7N_7	5-Aminotetrazole, compound with hydrazine	CNS	Isothiocyanato
		CN_2OS	Nitrosyl thiocyanate
		CN_4O_8	Tetranitromethane
CH_8N_2O	Hydrazine, compound with methanol	CN_6	5-Diazotetrazole
		CO	Carbon monoxide
$CH_8N_2O_3$	Ammonium carbonate	COS	Carbonyl sulfide
$CH_8N_2O_3S$	Methanesulfonic acid, hydrazine salt	CO_2	Carbon dioxide
$CH_8N_2O_5$	Urea, compound with H_2O_2	CO_3	Carbon oxide
		CP	
$CH_8N_2S_3$	Ammonium thio- carbonate	CS	Carbon monosulfide
		CS_2	Carbon disulfide

APPENDIX IV

The Number of Possible Carbon Compounds

In order to estimate the number of possible carbon compounds as a function of carbon number, an examination was made of the Formula Index of *Chemical Abstracts* and the number of index pages as a function of carbon number was recorded. This information is shown in Fig. AIV-1. The number of compounds listed in the index is a product of

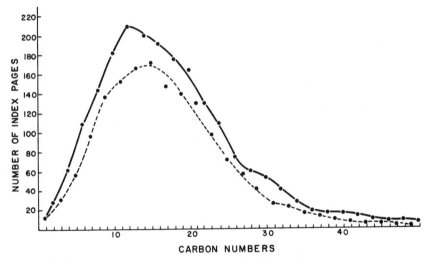

FIG. AIV-1. Graph indicating the number of index pages of carbon compounds as a function of the number of carbon atoms. Dashed lines are odd carbon numbers and solid lines are even carbon numbers.

two functions: the number of possible compounds and the fraction of those that have been studied. The first is an increasing function of carbon number, and the second is a decreasing function. The difference shown for odd and even compounds reflects the difference in the fraction studied. Most large carbon compounds studied are natural products where a preference for even numbers obtains. Hence, the even-number graph is raised above the odd-number graph.

The actual graph of carbon compounds versus carbon number must actually rise faster than the upper curve. The carbon-one value must be scaled to be greater than 234. The carbon-two value is therefore, considerably greater than 540. On *a priori* grounds, one would expect the number of two-carbon compounds to be appreciably larger than 540. If each one-carbon compound reacted with every other one-carbon compound to give at least one stable product, we would anticipate about 40,000 two-carbon compounds. In any case, as indicated in Chapter III, the number is large, but finite and denumerable.

APPENDIX V

Solar Spectral Irradiance Data

The wavelength λ is in microns, the mean zero air mass spectral-irradiance H_λ is in watts per square centimeter per micron, and P_λ is the percentage of the solar constant associated with wavelengths shorter than wavelength λ. The data are from F. S. Johnson, *J. Meteorol.* **11**, 431 (1954).

λ	H_λ	P_λ	λ	H_λ	P_λ
0.22	0.0030	0.02	0.37	0.133	6.36
0.225	0.0042	0.03	0.375	0.132	6.84
0.23	0.0052	0.05	0.38	0.123	7.29
0.235	0.0054	0.07	0.385	0.115	7.72
0.24	0.0058	0.09	0.39	0.112	8.13
0.245	0.0064	0.11	0.395	0.120	8.54
0.25	0.0064	0.13	0.40	0.154	9.03
0.255	0.010	0.16	0.405	0.188	9.65
0.26	0.013	0.20	0.41	0.194	10.3
0.265	0.020	0.27	0.415	0.192	11.0
0.27	0.025	0.34	0.42	0.192	11.7
0.275	0.022	0.43	0.425	0.189	12.4
0.28	0.024	0.51	0.43	0.178	13.0
0.285	0.034	0.62	0.435	0.182	13.7
0.29	0.052	0.77	0.44	0.203	14.4
0.295	0.063	0.98	0.445	0.215	15.1
0.30	0.061	1.23	0.45	0.220	15.9
0.305	0.067	1.43	0.455	0.219	16.7
0.31	0.076	1.69	0.46	0.216	17.5
0.315	0.082	1.97	0.465	0.215	18.2
0.32	0.085	2.26	0.47	0.217	19.0
0.325	0.102	2.60	0.475	0.220	19.8
0.33	0.115	3.02	0.48	0.216	20.6
0.335	0.111	3.40	0.485	0.203	21.3
0.34	0.111	3.80	0.49	0.199	22.0
0.345	0.117	4.21	0.495	0.204	22.8
0.35	0.118	4.63	0.50	0.198	23.5
0.355	0.116	5.04	0.505	0.197	24.2
0.36	0.116	5.47	0.51	0.196	24.9
0.365	0.129	5.89	0.515	0.189	25.6

λ	H_λ	P_λ	λ	H_λ	P_λ
0.52	0.187	26.3	1.4	0.0328	85.5
0.525	0.192	26.9	1.5	0.0267	87.6
0.53	0.195	27.6	1.6	0.0220	89.4
0.535	0.197	28.3	1.7	0.0182	90.83
0.54	0.198	29.0	1.8	0.0152	92.03
0.545	0.198	29.8	1.9	0.01274	93.02
0.55	0.195	30.5	2.0	0.01079	93.87
0.555	0.192	31.2	2.1	0.00917	94.58
0.56	0.190	31.8	2.2	0.00785	95.20
0.565	0.189	32.5	2.3	0.00676	95.71
0.57	0.187	33.2	2.4	0.00585	96.18
0.575	0.187	33.9	2.5	0.00509	96.57
0.58	0.187	34.5	2.6	0.00445	96.90
0.585	0.185	35.2	2.7	0.00390	97.21
0.59	0.184	35.9	2.8	0.00343	97.47
0.595	0.183	36.5	2.9	0.00303	97.72
0.60	0.181	37.2	3.0	0.00268	97.90
0.61	0.177	38.4	3.1	0.00230	98.08
0.62	0.174	39.7	3.2	0.00214	98.24
0.63	0.170	40.9	3.3	0.00191	98.39
0.64	0.166	42.1	3.4	0.00171	98.52
0.65	0.162	43.3	3.5	0.00153	98.63
0.66	0.159	44.5	3.6	0.00139	98.74
0.67	0.155	45.6	3.7	0.00125	98.83
0.68	0.151	46.7	3.8	0.00114	98.91
0.69	0.148	47.8	3.9	0.00103	98.99
0.70	0.144	48.8	4.0	0.00095	99.05
0.71	0.141	49.8	4.1	0.00087	99.13
0.72	0.137	50.8	4.2	0.00080	99.18
0.73	0.134	51.8	4.3	0.00073	99.23
0.74	0.130	52.7	4.4	0.00067	99.29
0.75	0.127	53.7	4.5	0.00061	99.33
0.80	0.1127	57.9	4.6	0.00056	99.38
0.85	0.1003	61.7	4.7	0.00051	99.41
0.90	0.0895	65.1	4.8	0.00048	99.45
0.95	0.0803	68.1	4.9	0.00044	99.48
1.0	0.0725	70.9	5.0	0.00042	99.51
1.1	0.0606	75.7	6.0	0.00021	99.74
1.2	0.0501	79.6	7.0	0.00012	99.86
1.3	0.0406	82.9			

Author Index

Numbers in parentheses are reference numbers and are included to assist in locating references in which the author's names are not mentioned in the text. Numbers in italics refer to pages on which the references are listed.

171

Subject Index

175